E. J. BALDRY.
DAME ALLAN'S SCHOOL
NEWCASTLE-on-TYNE.

# A GUIDE TO FIELD BIOLOGY

# A GUIDE TO FIELD BIOLOGY

*By*

JOHN SANKEY, B.Sc.

LONGMANS, GREEN AND CO.

LONDON • NEW YORK • TORONTO

LONGMANS, GREEN AND CO LTD
6 & 7 CLIFFORD STREET LONDON W I
THIBAULT HOUSE THIBAULT SQUARE CAPE TOWN
605–611 LONSDALE STREET MELBOURNE C I

LONGMANS, GREEN AND CO INC
55 FIFTH AVENUE NEW YORK 3

LONGMANS, GREEN AND CO
20 CRANFIELD ROAD TORONTO 16

ORIENT LONGMANS PRIVATE LTD
CALCUTTA BOMBAY MADRAS
DELHI HYDERABAD DACCA

*First published 1958*

*Made and printed in Great Britain by*
*William Clowes and Sons, Limited, London and Beccles*

# FOREWORD

"Faunists, as you observe, are too apt to acquiesce in bare
descriptions and a few synonyms: the reason is plain
because all that may be done at home in a man's study,
but the investigation of the life and conversation of
animals is a concern of much more trouble and difficulty,
and is not to be attained but by the active and inquisitive,
and by those that reside much in the country."

GILBERT WHITE: Letter to Daines Barrington:
Selborne, 1 August 1771

It is a curious thing that in Britain, with our long line of
great naturalists, the genuine love of nature revealed in our
finest art and literature, our sincere affection for country
pursuits and pastimes, for gardening, for plants and animals—
that in spite of all this, in so many of our schools the serious
study of living natural history as a part of the curriculum does
not figure at all and its apology is (or was until recently) so
often a text-book-ridden dead biology.

Some light may be thrown on this matter by a glance at the
history of the biological sciences during the last hundred years.
We are about to celebrate the centenary of the publication of
the *Origin of Species* by Charles Darwin (1859). That year
marks one of the great turning points in the history of thought
—the influence of the *Origin of Species* in every domain has
been stupendous—it is perhaps significant that it is the work
of a great field naturalist. There is evidence on almost every
page of some field observation and what is remarkable is the
number that are first-hand. The effect of Darwin's work on the
biological sciences—particularly on zoology—was immediate,
dramatic and profound. T. H. Huxley's biting retort to the
patronising cynicism of Wilberforce at the meeting of the

British Association at Oxford, in 1860, is classical. Although perhaps only "a storm in a Victorian teacup" (as Dr. Raven calls it) it served at least as good evolutionary publicity; Darwinism indeed was in the headlines. Of much greater importance was the fact that biologists began to ask themselves what really constitutes a *species*, so that for some fifty years they forsook the field and applied themselves to exacting tasks in museums and laboratories, working up more critical and precise descriptions of specimens and leading eventually to a more accurate classification; this was a very necessary stage in the development of the sciences of botany and zoology, for the most careful and painstaking observations of living organisms in the field are useless if their identity is not known precisely. As Elton has pointed out, this was the defect of much of the older natural history and brought the subject into disrepute, particularly among zoologists. It was unfortunate for biology teaching that the great educational movement, following the Act of 1870, should have coincided with this phase of the indoor systematisation of the biological sciences for, if biology found a place at all—the physical sciences were predominant—the emphasis was on the examination of dead specimens in the classroom and not on the observation of living plants and animals in the field.

The quickening of the spirit that was to infuse new life into biology came from the botanists at the turn of the century with the development of modern plant ecology, of which A. G. Tansley was subsequently the protagonist. Parallel to and closely linked with the development of plant ecology was the Regional Survey Movement inspired by Patrick Geddes. A great impetus was thus given to the study of the environment —of plants, of animals and of man—and now that the systematists had overhauled the classification of animals and plants, precise identification became possible and indeed imperative. Field work was to become academically respectable. But we have still a long way to go at present before it permeates our system of education as a whole. (Until it does there can surely be no possibility of any clear general realisation of what the effects of human over-population upon the environment really entail for mankind: nor will Science be forced to find a remedy for the welcome removal of the Malthusian checks which its rapid advance has brought about.)

Mr. John Sankey has been in the very spearhead of the movement designed to achieve this end. His experience as a teacher of field biology must be unique; for more than ten years, day in and day out, he has been conducting groups of students of all ages in the field sciences: what is significant is that this instruction in field and laboratory has been based upon, and continuously allied to, personal ecological investigations which have been published as original papers in the transactions of several of our leading Learned Societies. I hope that his *Guide to Field Biology*—the epitome of so much valuable experience—may prove to be a useful vade-mecum to those who, in spite of all difficulties, are intent on undertaking first-hand observation and experiment in the field.

I have come between the author and his readers long enough; I apologise to both if I have proved myself guilty of a foible of which even the great Dr. Samuel Johnson was not entirely innocent—the temptation "to point a moral, or adorn a tale".

F. H. C. BUTLER

# PREFACE

This book is addressed to everyone who is interested in plants and animals. It is hoped that it will be helpful to teachers, training-college students, boys and girls of sixth-form standard and amateur naturalists. It is intended as a *guide* and in no sense aims at completeness, that indeed would not be possible in a volume of this size, and with our rapidly increasing knowledge about plants and animals in their natural habitats. The need for such a guide has been felt by the writer during his teaching at the Centres of the Field Studies Council.*

It is the aim of this book to outline the more important principles of land and fresh-water ecology and to introduce methods used in field biology. With this in mind sections on Geology and Pedology have been included, as well as a number of selected suggestions for field studies. Information is given in the appendices on literature, elementary museum techniques and other matters ancillary to field work. These are too often ignored in a formal curriculum of biological training, and without guidance the amateur naturalist often experiences difficulty in finding such information.

It has been pointed out (J. H. P. Sankey, *School Science Review*, No. 124. p. 394, June 1953) that the downs, woodlands, marshes, waste-ground and ponds and streams are more familiar to the majority of people who go out from the laboratory or their study, than are the coast, estuaries or the sea itself. Emphasis has therefore been given to terrestrial ecology. It is the writer's hope that this little book will do something to promote and further interest in the scientific study of plants and animals in the field.

* Formerly Council for the Promotion of Field Studies, Head Office: Balfour House, 112 Finsbury Pavement, London, E.C.2.

It is not possible to mention the many authors from whom I
have drawn information, or all my students at the Juniper Hall
Field Centre who have often unknowingly been the subject of
ideas and experiments. I am grateful for all their assistance.
It is a pleasure to acknowledge the help of Mr. D. G. Brown
of Monkton Combe School, Bath, with certain illustrations.
I am also indebted to all who have aided me in various other
ways, especially to Mr. B. W. Avery, Dr. S. Graham Brade-
Birks and Professor Joe L. White of Purdue University,
Indiana, who have kindly helped with pedological problems;
to Dr. Francis Rose for assistance with botanical matters and
Mr. S. Derek Woods for guidance with the presentation of the
chemical aspects of pH. It is a pleasure to acknowledge also
the assistance of Dr. D. Arthur and Dr. J. L. Cloudsley-
Thompson both of the University of London, King's College.
Mr. C. C. Fagg has given me kindly advice in a number of
matters, and Miss I. A. Fagg gave me valuable secretarial
assistance. Mr. F. H. C. Butler, Founder and Educational
Adviser of The Field Studies Council, has been good enough
to write a foreword; his enthusiasm inspired the idea of this
book. Finally my publishers, Longmans, Green & Co. Ltd., at
all times have given me courteous and helpful advice for which
I am most appreciative.

JOHN SANKEY

Field Studies Council,
Juniper Hall Field Centre,
Dorking,
Surrey.
*February*, 1958.

# CONTENTS

# LIST OF ILLUSTRATIONS

2

## Section A

# GEOLOGY AND FIELD BIOLOGY

Geology is the study of the earth's crust. Strictly speaking it is the study of rocks, and the study of soils is called Pedology. Geology and Pedology are closely related.

The chief constituent of soils is rock material and nearly all plants are directly dependent on soil. Animals in turn are dependent on plants. Thus rocks are fundamentally important to the biologist who should have at least a working knowledge of Geology and Pedology.

Most people think of rock as something hard. Some rocks *are* hard and can only be broken by a sharp blow from a heavy hammer. Others are soft and can be easily disintegrated with a penknife like some sandstones which are excavated by sand martins. Clay holds water, but loose kinds of sandstones let it drain through very readily. Limestones, of which Chalk is one, are alkaline or basic, and react when a drop of dilute hydrochloric acid is poured on to them giving off carbon dioxide as small bubbles. Quartzites do not behave in this way, they are themselves acid. These few examples show that rocks may have very different physical and chemical properties, and these properties are important in the study of the distribution of plants and animals and their relationships to their surroundings (as well as to each other)—a subject called *Ecology*.

There are various branches of Geology; to the biologist the most important are:

*Mineralogy* and *Crystallography*—the study of the physical and chemical constitution of rocks, and of the individual minerals of which each rock is composed.

1

*Stratigraphy*—the position of the rocks in relation to one another and their *dip* or inclination to the horizontal.

*Geomorphology* and *Hydrography* (together constituting *Physical Geology*)—the effect of Geology on surface relief and conditions.

*Palaeontology* and *Palaeobotany*—the study of fossil remains of animals and plants. These have little direct bearing on present-day animal and plant ecology, but some rocks are largely composed of fossil remains, and it is their mineral composition, rather than the fossil forms, that is important to the ecologist.

Field biologists should make themselves acquainted with the geological map of their district and learn how to interpret it in terms of Mineralogy, Stratigraphy and Geomorphology. In this book space will only allow emphasis on the more essential studies of Physical Geology, and the chemical and physical aspects of Crystallography and Mineralogy.

All rocks originated by solidification of molten material from the earth's interior. When this material, after cooling, has undergone no further change, the resulting rocks are *crystalline*, and these are found mainly in the west and north of the British Isles, and often in hilly districts where in the remote past there has been volcanic activity.

Volcanoes are places in the earth's crust where the molten material has escaped to the surface, and as it cooled formed a cone. It may, however, have just poured out on to the surface from long fissures in the crust. If this material cooled slowly, large crystals formed, e.g. the basalts of the Giant's Causeway, but if it cooled quickly, time only allowed small crystals to grow, or the material may have become amorphous like pumice. Large areas of crystalline rock occur on the earth's surface, and it is believed that most of the British Isles is underlain by this type—the so-called Palaeozoic Platform—which has been laid bare in places by the removal of overlying sedimentary rocks (see below). This platform was not formed by volcanoes, but by the gradual cooling of large quantities of liquid magma *in situ*.

During the course of ages some crystalline rocks have been subjected to weathering. The crystals have been broken down by the action of water, sun, frost and other agents. The resulting mineral particles have been transported by rivers—and occasionally by wind—and in nearly all cases find their way into the sea where they settle slowly on the bottom, forming a deposit which in time may attain great thickness. The coarser grains of rock material come to rest first on the continental shelf nearer land, but the finer grains are carried further out, and are usually deposited in deeper water. These marine deposits have been consolidated into rocks and raised up thus forming dry land. Some have been eroded away again by the agents of denudation, and the material from these rocks has been carried back to the sea to form, by similar processes of consolidation and uplifting, other marine deposits, which in time have become other rocks. It is probable that the material which forms these *sedimentary rocks* has been transported from land to sea many times in the countless ages of our earth's history.

In general, sedimentary rocks are softer and more easily weathered than igneous rocks. Water percolates through more readily and their contribution to the mineral fraction of the soil is made more quickly than is the case with igneous rocks.

During past ages the movement of great ice sheets has removed soil and rock over much of the country, and has mixed and transported them to other areas. In this way *glacial deposits* have been formed. During the recent or Quaternary Ice Age large deposits of glacial material were spread over the British Isles. An area north of an approximate line from London to Bristol, was covered by the ice sheet during maximum glaciation. The deposits left by the ice are relatively unconsolidated, and often very mixed in character. Rock from other districts can be recognised in them, and so the direction of movements of the ice sheets can be traced. The extent of the latter is basic to an understanding of the present-day distribution of the flora and fauna. Glacial deposits, river gravels, alluvium, *head* and other superficial deposits come under the term *drift* which the biologist should regard as rock.

Wind has also been responsible for the formation of some superficial deposits—so called because they have been laid down comparatively recently on top of the older crystalline or sedimentary rocks. These are called *loess*, and they give rise to a very fertile and valuable soil. The few deposits in Great Britain occur mostly in parts of East Anglia.

*Metamorphic* rocks have been formed by the effect of heat and pressure on a sedimentary, or more rarely, on an igneous rock. An *intrusion* of hot molten material may have modified the surrounding rocks through which it came. For practical purposes rocks formed in this way are usually biologically unimportant. When, however, folding and pressure caused metamorphosis, which may have taken place on a relatively large scale, the resulting rock may give rise to a soil chemically and physically quite different from that of the original rock.

These three kinds of rock—igneous, sedimentary (including drift, or superficial deposits) and metamorphic, are the sources of the mineral fraction of the soil. In this respect their biological importance is twofold. Chemically they supply substances necessary for plant and animal life. Physically they play an important rôle in the natural drainage of soils, which itself can only be understood by considering also the physical nature of the underlying rocks.

Many of the substances needed by plants and animals are contained in the rocks which can therefore be regarded as a reservoir for these chemicals. But they are more directly obtained from the soil. Relatively pure kinds of rocks like some *limestones* and acid *sandstones* are more limited in their chemical contribution to the necessities of plant and animal life.

The physical nature of a rock determines its ability to withhold or release water and mineral solutions. To this is related its rate of disintegration, and therefore the quantitative contribution it can make to the mineral fraction of the soil. The nature of the drainage in turn is important in regulating soil temperature. A well-drained soil overlying a relatively porous rock is known to the horticulturalist and farmer as an "early soil", while a moisture-laden heavy soil overlying clay is a "late soil".

Drainage of rocks and soils is described in general terms such as impeded, normal and excessive (see p. 15). In a rock having impeded drainage the mineral grains are in close contact. Such rocks have no, or very few, cracks or fissures. In clays the size of the particles is invariably very small, and this assists in the retention of water which is held on the grains by surface tension, though clays suffer superficially in times of long drought. Capillary water, that is, water held by capillary forces between the grains, cannot circulate freely. The passage of water within such rocks is strictly limited. Clays and some hard igneous crystalline rocks have impeded drainage.

In marked contrast are those rocks in which the grain size is larger and through which water can readily percolate, or in which fissures are developed to such an extent that water passes freely through. There is a marked increase in drainage corresponding to increase in grain size and state of compactness of the rock; here surface tension forces play a minor part in water retention. Many sandstones and glacial gravels, for instance, show excessive drainage.

Between these two extremes is normal drainage in which the rock retains a certain amount of water and never dries out completely.

Factors other than its physical characteristics influence the nature of a rock. The inclination or dip may encourage drainage, especially if the rock is loosely bedded in inclined planes. The nature of the underlying beds may be important in retaining or releasing water, even if the rock itself is naturally very porous, as in the case of a sandstone overlying clay.

Drainage is impeded in a rock with harder layers, for example the "iron pans" in some sandstones. These may completely stop drainage so that an acid bog becomes established on the surface. These bands of ironstone must not be confused with the "B horizon" pans of podsol soils (see p. 25) which may cause similar conditions on the surface.

Even a thin band of relatively non-porous rock, like parts of the Grinstead Clay in the Tunbridge Wells Sands (Lower Cretaceous, S.E. England), may be sufficient to throw out a spring line on a hillside, or it may retain a water reservoir within the rock. If the relatively non-porous rock is only developed locally the resulting water reservoir forms a *perched water table* or *perched water line*. (The term "line" or perhaps "horizon" is preferable to "table" since the surface of the underground reservoir, which can only be shown in profile, tends to follow the surface relief and is rarely flat as implied by "table".)

The water line rises and falls according to the rainfall, and in some areas to the demands made upon underground water by water-works and wells.

Coal mining may cause subsidence and the surface may be lowered to such an extent as to become flooded. This has happened in the neighbourhood of the Chislet Colliery in Kent where a large area of the river Stour has become a very fine stretch of marshland with extensive patches of open water. This area is noted for its bird and other wild life.

It is only a matter of convenience that the rocks and soils are given separate treatment in this book. The two are inseparably linked as will be seen in the discussion of soil properties.

## Section B

# SOILS

## I. INTRODUCTION

Soil is a mixture of mineral particles, humus, air and water. Soils vary, even in a very short distance, and this variation in kind and property, and a knowledge of the factors which cause it, must be studied by all field biologists.

Civilisation depends on soil. The increasing world population demands more intensive and extended areas of cultivation to meet the growing food shortage. Humanity is faced with a big ecological problem. Soil study or Pedology is not just an academic subject. A knowledge and appreciation of soils is as vitally necessary to the biologist as it is to every farmer and gardener and, in fact, to everybody—except Eskimos! Soil is the most important raw material which man handles and all plants and animals are dependent on it.

## II. "DISSECTION" OF THE SOIL

### i. *The Geology of Soil*

Much of the material of soils (except peat) came originally from rock; this is the *mineral fraction*. It consists principally of two compounds—silica or quartz (silicon dioxide) and potassium aluminium silicate of which the minerals orthoclase, felspar and biotite mica, characteristically containing iron and magnesium, are the most important. Other chemicals form only a small fraction of the mineral constituents of the soil, but carbonates—usually a form of calcium carbonate—are quite

7

distinct, and often impart characteristic properties to the soils overlying Chalk, Oolitic and Carboniferous Limestone.

The rocks are an almost unlimited reservoir of chemicals needed by plant and animal life. But these food substances are released and made available very slowly. They may be abundant, yet in a non-available form in the rock, or as grains in the soil. These chemicals are released and made available for plant food by a series of complex processes collectively called *weathering*.

### ii. *Weathering*

By its continual action weathering produces changes in both the soil and rock. Through wetting and drying, heating and cooling, and changes produced chemically, as well as the part played by the micro-organisms of the soil and the larger plants and animals, rock is disintegrated and its products contribute to the formation of soil.

The chief agents of weathering can be summarised as follows:

### (a) *Physical*

1. *Heating* and *cooling*, including frost action. These cause expansion and contraction of minerals and tend to separate them into individual grains.

2. *Wetting* and *drying* which also cause physical disintegration.

3. *Mechanical removal of substances* by percolating water.

### (b) *Chemical*

1. *Hydration*—the addition of water to a substance. This is a chemical reaction forming a new compound. An example is the change of hematite (oxide of iron), which forms a series of closely related minerals according to the amount of combining water. This process causes expansion of the minerals and so helps to disintegrate the rock and soil.

2. *Hydrolysis*—also a chemical reaction between water and a mineral. Unlike hydration, involving a simple addition of water, the process of hydrolysis is more complicated, and

results in entirely new chemical compounds, and it is probably more important in the disintegration of some minerals in the soil, releasing and making available mineral foods to plants. Hydrolysis of orthoclase to give kaolinite (found in china clay) is a well-known example.

3. *Oxidation*—the addition of oxygen to a compound. Oxygen occurs in soil air and soil water. Oxidation is usually one step in a series of weathering processes, for example, conversion of ferrous carbonate into limonite.

4. *Reduction* is in a sense the reverse of oxidation. Oxygen is removed from a compound. This usually happens in rocks and soils where there is a deficiency of oxygen, as in waterlogged areas, or where much decaying vegetation is present as in a bog. Removal of oxygen may form new minerals and can also cause disintegration.

5. *Carbonation*. When carbon dioxide is dissolved in water a weak solution of carbonic acid is formed. Carbon dioxide in the air becomes dissolved in falling rain, or it may be taken up in the soil water from organic matter from which it is evolved during decomposition of plant and animal remains. The carbonic acid has a solvent action, especially on bases. Hence limestones and basic soils are particularly susceptible to carbonation. Removal of calcareous " cement " causes a rock to disintegrate, as does also removal of basic elements from the upper layers of a soil. The latter process is discussed more fully under the section dealing with podsols (see p. 25).

(c) *Biotic*

Animals and plants, dead and alive, are in a sense, agents of weathering. Apart from direct influence by mechanical disturbance and other processes in the soil and rock, they facilitate entrance of air and water and so contribute to the chemical and physical processes discussed above.

Roots of plants expand as they grow, and by pressure alone can disintegrate a rock. Root tips secrete various substances, one of which is an acid which dissolves basic minerals with which it comes in contact.

The evolution of carbon dioxide from decaying plant and animal remains has been noted in the process of carbonation. Bacteria and fungi are largely responsible for this decay, and must be regarded as contributory to factors of weathering.

Fertility of soil is increased by the presence of nitrogen fixing bacteria; some occur in the root nodules of leguminous plants. The bacteria are able to extract and fix nitrogen from the soil atmosphere. This nitrogen ultimately increases plant growth, and therefore the humus content of the soil. Carbonation may thus be increased (see p. 9).

Burrowing animals—earthworms, some millipedes, moles, rabbits, badgers, etc., and many smaller arthropods, such as insects, are capable of mechanically disturbing the soil. Their dead bodies and droppings contribute to humus formation. Earthworms speed this process by removal of leaves from the surface into the soil, where bacteria cause their decay. Worms also turn out soil on to the surface where it is subjected to heating, cooling, wetting and drying, so that the mineral grains are further broken down.

In a study of weathering of rocks and soils all available climatic data should be noted. Rainfall is especially important. If direct observations cannot be made, relevant figures are usually available, free of charge, from the Meteorological Office.* Their records cover most of Great Britain and sufficiently localised information can nearly always be obtained from them.

Two important factors in soil formation have been discussed —the rocks and the weather. The origin of soils can now be studied.

### iii. *The Origin of Soils*

Lichens are usually the first plants to colonise bare rock, or young or immature soils. As the rock disintegrates, humus from the plant life is mixed with the mineral particles together

* The Director, The Meteorological Office (M.O. 3), Headstone Drive, Harrow, Middlesex.

with water and air. The rudiments of a soil are formed. It is still immature, and on the tops of high mountains, usually in exposed positions, immature soils can be found. They are usually called "skeletal soils". By continuing weathering of the rock and further additions of plant remains a deeper soil is formed. Herbaceous plants then begin to colonise, and the process of humus addition is hastened by the contribution made by the dead remains of larger plants. Eventually the full soil population—protozoa, earthworms, insects, etc.—is established.

In a limestone, sandstone or clay quarry, where there is usually no covering of river gravel or other superficial deposit it will be seen that the soil is formed directly from the under-lying rock. Pieces of this can often be seen in the soil, and individual mineral grains can be matched with those in the parent material below. Such soils are said to be formed *in situ*. Other soils are *derived* and are commonly found in valleys where their mineral content has been transported from other areas by a river. They are sometimes referred to as *alluvial soils*.

Mineral particles tend to move down hill under the influence of gravity, and a derived soil may be formed at the foot of a hill. In other areas wind-blown particles (*loess*) form derived soils.


### iv. *Topography or Surface Relief*

Certain soil properties depend partly on surface relief of the immediate neighbourhood. Aspect is also important. In this country a north-facing slope is colder than one facing south, and a soil at a high altitude is colder than one near sea level.

The maximum slope on which a more or less continuous sward (see p. 39) can grow is about 36°, and at about 60° a sand dune begins to slide. The surface, flat or uneven, undu-lating, ridged, etc., is important. Small hollows may retain moisture in which different plants and animals can live.

In a survey the exact angle and direction of slope from the horizontal should be stated (fig. 1). Height is given, preferably in metres, above sea level—O.D. (Ordnance Datum.)

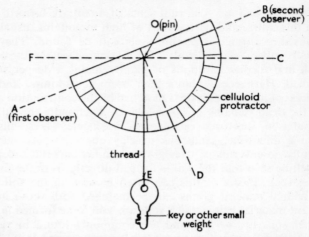

FIG. 1.—A simple clinometer. To find the angle of slope the
observer at A holds the protractor vertically and sights it on the
eyes of a second observer B whose eyes must be the same height
above the ground as A's (alternatively a marked pole can be
used). A then grips the thread and protractor and the angle
DOE which, since DOE=COB=AOF, is the *angle of elevation*
(up-slope) or *of depression* (down-slope).

[*Note*: to find the height ($x$) of a tree or cliff, stand a known distance ($d$) away
from the base—preferably 10 m (30 ft.) or further; measure the angle ($a$)
between the ground and line of sight to the top (i.e. the angle DOE). Then
$x = d \times \tan a +$ height from ground to clinometer. (On sloping ground take
the average angle measured from the same distance on each side of the tree).]

Topography may be important in determining the type of
soil drainage; this is discussed in the next section.

## v. *Drainage*

Does water lie on the surface? Does the soil feel dry? Is it
mottled brown below the surface? Can water be reached with
a spade or auger (fig. 2)? These questions are intimately connected with the natural drainage of the soil which involves a
consideration of mineral particle size, topography and rock type.

The smaller a particle the greater is its surface area compared
with its volume. By means of surface tension water is retained

on a particle. Therefore soils with small particles hold more moisture than those with bigger ones. Moreover the individual grains pack more closely in a small-grained soil, and there is less likelihood of water loss through evaporation towards the surface, or by drainage through the soil. This "heavy" kind of

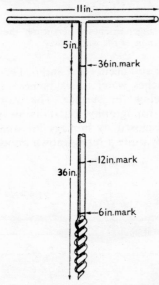

Fig. 2.—The soil auger. The instrument is made of steel. In use it is screwed 6 in. into the ground and pulled out. After the first 6 in. of soil have been examined and discarded, it is put in the same hole and screwed in to 12 in., and so on to a depth of 36 in.

soil tends to show impeded drainage, and may often be water-logged. In a "light" soil, where the particles are bigger, surface tension cannot act so readily, and there is more space between the grains which permits evaporation and better drainage.

Mineral particle or grain size is therefore fundamentally important when considering drainage. The system of classification of soils described on p. 18 is based on grain sizes.

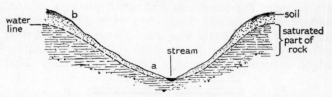

FIG. 3.—At *a* the auger reaches water nearer the surface than at *b* because of the height of the water line.

In fig. 3 a similar soil occurs at *a* and *b*. The former is wetter and the augur reaches water at six inches whereas at *b* it is nearly two feet below the surface. The water line tends to follow the surface topography, but falls away on the higher ground. This is disclosed by borings for wells, and in some parts of the country quite a lot is known about the water line.

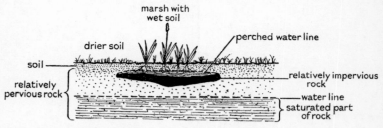

FIG. 4.—A small patch of relatively impervious rock like clay impedes drainage and maintains a perched water line.

In fig. 4 a local obstruction—an iron pan—causes a limited area of swamp to develop above it. This is a perched water line. Local bands of clay produce a similar effect on the surface. Slope assists surface drainage as water moves downhill and less penetrates into the ground. This varies according to the nature of the soil. Ground water also responds to an incline, and in a light soil may drain away readily.

It is useful to have a scale for recording drainage. A handy and sufficiently accurate one for use in the field is:

1—excessive, soil very dry (light soils).
2—free.
3—normal.
4—deficient.
5—impeded (heavy clay soils.)

At the beginning of this section reference was made to mottling of soil. A brown mottled soil is a sign of impeded drainage. Iron in the form of ferric oxide is a common chemical. When water accumulates in a soil it drives out air. Certain bacteria then begin to get oxygen by reduction of the ferric oxide to the ferrous state. When air comes back some of the iron is reoxidised giving a mottled appearance. Local names such as "crownstone", "cat's brains" and "shrave" are used to describe this.

### vi. *Soil Reaction or pH*

From discussion of the mineral section and weathering of soils, it will be understood that the size of the mineral particles depends on the amount of weathering undergone and on their chemical nature. In general the greater the weathering the smaller will be the mineral grains. Theoretically there would be no limit to the reduction of their size till they are broken down into individual atoms. For the immediate purposes only the individual molecules and larger colloidal fractions, which are weathered down from the mineral grains, need to be considered. The latter can thus be divided into larger particles which, though weathering very slowly, contribute very little to the soil at any given time. But the other particles are exceedingly small, and together with the humus present in the soil form the *colloidal* or *weathering complex*.

Basic elements in the soil, the chief of which is usually calcium, enter into loose combination with the weathering complex, but will dissociate from it in the presence of excess acid. The amount of calcium that can be given up by the weathering complex is called the *exchangeable base*. In limestone soils the weathering complex is completely saturated,

3

and the soil is said to be *base saturated*. When the soil is not completely base saturated, dissociated positively charged hydrogen ions (cations), are present in the soil water. The positively charged hydrogen ions are used to determine soil reaction. In pure water, or a neutral solution, the concentration of Hydrogen ions equals that of negatively charged Hydroxyl ions and in each case is $10^{-7}$, i.e. $(H^+) = (OH^-) = 10^{-7}$ and the product of these concentrations is $10^{-14}$. This value is constant for all aqueous solutions. An acid solution therefore is one in which the concentration of Hydrogen $H^+$ ions exceeds that of the Hydroxyl $H^-$ ion. Conversely an alkaline solution is one where the concentration of Hydroxyl ions exceeds that of Hydrogen ions. Thus if the concentration of H ions is $10^{-8}$ gm. ions per litre, that of OH will be $10^{-14} \div 10^{-8} = 10^{-6}$. An alternative method of expressing Hydrogen ion concentration is known as the pH * scale and is calculated thus

$$pH = \log_{10} \frac{1}{H \text{ ion concentration}}$$

In the above example $pH = \log_{10}\dfrac{1}{10^{-8}} = 8$

Biologists attach importance to the pH of soil solutions and aquatic habitats. There are various methods differing in their degree of accuracy for measuring pH. These are discussed on p. 116.

pH controls a number of other biological processes, for example, the availability of certain mineral salts required by plants. Some plants and animals tolerate only a limited pH range.

### vii. *Colour*

The colour of the soil is a distinctive property, and often indicates its chemical or mineral constituents—the two sources

* *p* stands for the German word Partialdruck = partial pressure ( S.P.L. Sörensen, 1909).

from which soil colour is derived. Organic matter, as well as an excess of iron or manganese, may impart a dark colour to soil. Iron compounds, depending on their degree of oxidation, gives rise to yellows, reds and greens. Under waterlogged conditions the soil is bluish (see p. 27). Calcium imparts a whitish tinge to the soil. Other minerals occasionally produce other colours.

Attempts have been made to standardise soil colours, but owing to variable factors such as moisture content, intensity and nature of light in which the soil is examined, only a general approximation can be made. It is best therefore to use only the following conventional colours—black, brown, grey, purple, red and yellow. These can be qualified by such adjectives as light, dark, mottled, etc., and by a combination of any of the standard colours themselves, e.g. greyish-yellow. It is important to avoid such descriptions as "wine coloured", "magenta", etc. These rarely assist in conveying the colour and may cause confusion.

## viii. *The Soil-profile*

Most people have seen the side of a sand, clay or limestone quarry, or the side of a trench dug for a drain, or road or railway cutting. The soil on top differs from the rock below. One may grade into the other, or there may be a series of well-marked colour changes or differences in texture. This side-view of the soil and rock is the *profile* or *section*. If no profile is available it can be studied from a specially dug pit or by the use of the soil auger (see fig. 2). The soil profile shows some of the characteristics already discussed, such as the differently coloured horizons and pH. Its study gives information about natural drainage, and, from it, evidence of its origin can be deduced. The profile is a summary of the properties of the soil, and the classification of a soil in the *series* is based on its profile. The soil series is the equivalent of a genus in biology (see p. 123). Much has been done to advance the study of soil series but there is still much scope for further work. For biological purposes identification of soil types (equivalent to a species, see p. 123) is more important and is dealt with in sub-section III below.

When recording a profile, a full description of each horizon down to the underlying rock, must be given. Some profiles of British soils are described on pp. 22–7.

These eight generic or soil series characteristics should be studied in every comprehensive botanical or zoological survey from an appropriate number of profiles examined in the field.

## III. IDENTIFICATION OF SOIL TYPES

Soil types are identified by their textural properties which are applicable to all horizons. Several classifications are in use, but one, based on the American system, is particularly useful to biologists, because it is sufficiently accurate to be easily used in the field. No apparatus is needed.

Recognition of soil types is based on the relative proportions of mineral grain sizes which are gauged as follows:

| | | | |
|---|---|---|---|
| Fine gravel . | 2–1 mm | average | diameter |
| Coarse sand . | 1–0·5 mm | ,, | ,, |
| Medium sand | 0·5–0·25 mm | ,, | ,, |
| Fine sand. . | 0·25–0·10 mm | ,, | ,, |
| Very fine sand | 0·10–0·05 mm | ,, | ,, |
| Silt . . . | 0·05–0·002 mm | ,, | ,, |
| Clay . . . less than 0·002 mm | ,, | ,, | |

Two other standards of particle size are sometimes employed but the one given above—the New American System—is in general use.

The quantity of each grain-size group in a soil sample can be determined by mechanical analysis in the laboratory, see Kilmer, V. J. and Alexander, L. T., "Methods of making mechanical analysis of soils", *Soil Science*, Vol. 68, pp. 15–24 (1949). The relative proportions can also be found with enough accuracy for field purposes by the feel and appearance of the soil.

This is a useful means of recognising any of the twenty soil types, because soil texture depends on the relative proportions of clay, silt and sand. With practice these proportions can be determined to an accuracy of about $\pm 5\%$.

The table on p. 20, gives the proportions of sand silt and clay in this soil classification. As the heavy mineral fraction of soils is small, the figures are referable to weight or volume. In practice they are obtained by weight.

For determination of soil texture a standardised method is used. The soil should be in a slightly moist condition, that is, neither waterlogged nor very dry—a condition in which seeds would grow and thrive. If the soil is wet—and not merely moist—allowances must be made when considering certain features, especially its power of cohesion, and if excessively dry it must be slightly moistened.

A quantity of the soil is moulded in the hand, and small amounts are passed through the thumb and index finger, and reference is made to the following key (summarised on p. 118):

*I.* Is the soil gritty but not sticky? If the answer is "yes" go to Section A. If not go to *II.* Note that a gritty sensation is imparted by the feel of ordinary sea-shore or builder's sand.

*II.* Is the soil sticky and/or silky but not gritty? If so go to Section B. If not, refer to *III.* Note that a silky feeling is to be taken literally—it gives the impression of a smooth creamy paste, or of flour.

*III.* Is the soil sticky and gritty? If so, go to Section C. If not the soil must come under Section *IV.*

*IV.* The soil is neither gritty, nor silky nor sticky—this identifies it as LOAM.

SECTION A

Can the soil be formed into a cohesive ball under *gentle* pressure in the hand? If so, refer to sub-section (*a*), if not, to (*b*).

(*a*) The soil can be formed into a cohesive ball. The four soils in this section are identified by the size of the visible particles.

*Table of proportions of gravel, sand, silt and clay in soils*

With less than 20% clay

**SANDS** Less than 15% silt and clay
- COARSE SAND: 35% or more fine gravel and coarse sand, less than 50% fine and very fine sand.
- SAND: 35% or more fine gravel, coarse and medium sand, less than 50% fine and very fine sand.
- FINE SAND: 50% or more fine or very fine sand.
- VERY FINE SAND: 50% or more very fine sand.

**LOAMY SANDS** 15–20% silt and clay
- LOAMY COARSE SAND: 35% or more fine gravel and coarse sand, less than 35% fine and very fine sand.
- LOAMY SAND: 35% or more fine gravel, coarse and medium sand, less than 35% fine and very fine sand.
- LOAMY FINE SAND: 35% or more fine and very fine sand.
- LOAMY VERY FINE SAND: 35% or more very fine sand.

**SANDY LOAMS** 20–50% silt and clay
- COARSE SANDY LOAM: 45% or more fine gravel and coarse sand.
- SANDY LOAM: 25% or more fine gravel, coarse and medium sand, less than 35% very fine sand.
- FINE SANDY LOAM: 50% or more fine sand, less than 25% fine gravel, coarse and medium sand.
- VERY FINE SANDY LOAM: 35% or more very fine sand.

**LOAM and SILT LOAM** 50% or more silt and clay
- LOAM: 30–50% silt and 30–50% sand.
- SILT LOAM: 50% or more silt, less than 50% sand.
- SILTY LOAM: 50% or more silt and clay, less than 20–30% sand.
- SANDY SILT LOAM: 30–50% sand.

**CLAY LOAMS** 20–30% Clay
- SANDY CLAY LOAM: less than 30% silt, 50–80% sand.
- CLAY LOAM: 20–50% silt, 20–50% sand.
- SILTY CLAY LOAM: 50–80% silt, less than 30% sand.

**CLAYS** 30% or more clay
- CLAY: less than 50% silt, less than 50% sand.

1. Soil particles of type sea-shore or builder's sand size—SANDY LOAM.

2. Particles markedly coarser than 1 (the finer types of aquarium "gravel")—COARSE SANDY LOAM.

3. Particles markedly finer than 1—FINE SANDY LOAM.

4. Particles barely visible to the naked eye—(silver sand)—VERY FINE SANDY LOAM.

(*b*) The soil cannot be formed into a cohesive ball.

This section is now subdivided into two:

Does the soil leave a well-defined mark when *gently* rubbed on to clean skin? If not, refer to sub-section (*aa*), if so to (*bb*). The four soils in each of these sections are again identified by grain size:

(*aa*) The soil does not mark clean skin.

1. Particles are of type sea-shore size—SAND.

2. Particles markedly coarser than 1—COARSE SAND.

3. Particles markedly finer than 1—FINE SAND.

4. Particles barely visible to naked eye—VERY FINE SAND.

(*bb*) The soil marks clean skin.

1. Particles are of type sea-shore size—LOAMY SAND.

2. Particles markedly coarser than 1—LOAMY COARSE SAND.

3. Particles markedly finer than 1—LOAMY FINE SAND.

4. Particles barely visible to naked eye—LOAMY VERY FINE SAND.

SECTION B

The two sub-sections depend on whether the soil can be *polished* or not when rubbed between finger and thumb. If there is a *smooth* light-reflecting surface, the soil is polished. Choose between (*a*) and (*b*).

(*a*) Soil cannot be polished between fingers.

Then select between:

1. Soil clearly silky (see *II*, p. 19)—SILT LOAM.

2. Soil not clearly silky—SILTY LOAM.

(*b*) Soil can be polished between fingers.

This group has three textural grades separated by their degree of resistance to deformation when a small sample of the soil is pushed and moulded between the fingers.

1. Easily deformed—SILTY CLAY LOAM.
2. Deformed with difficulty—CLAY LOAM.
3. Very resistant—CLAY.

In practice clay is met with only as a rock and when it has been brought to the surface by disturbance or removal of the soil.

SECTION C

The separation of these two textural grades presents no difficulty. Both are uncommon.

1. Cannot be polished between fingers—SANDY SILT LOAM.
2. Can be polished between fingers—SANDY CLAY LOAM.

A little practice is required in the identification of textural properties, comparison of types is important, but once the characters have been mastered, this system of soil classification can be used with speed and accuracy in the field.

Soils are not separable in the sense that most plants and animals are distinct species. One soil type may grade into another. Doubt may arise about a soil being one of two closely allied types, for example, a loamy coarse sand and a coarse loamy sand. In practice, and from the biological point of view, it matters little which of the two is recorded, as they are closely related in their clay, silt and sand proportions (see p. 20) and have very similar physical properties.

## IV. SOILS OF GREAT BRITAIN

### i. *Introduction*

Three main groups of soils occur in this country—four if peat is included on the grounds that it is a medium in which plants grow. The following accounts refer to mature soils, but immature soils are not uncommon, especially where the ground has been disturbed by human activity, or where glacial activity, or river action has removed the original soil comparatively recently and exposed the rock. Immature soils are found in regions where recent deposits have accumulated, or have been made artificially, and in exposed places, like mountain tops too unstable to support permanent vegetation (except possibly lichens).

Some soils show different phases—shallow or deep for example; others may be truncated, that is, the upper horizons have been removed by water action, land-slide or by human interference. If the eight points discussed on pp. 7–18 are taken into account it is possible to assign any soil to one of these groups.

## ii. *Brown Earths—or Brown Forest Earths*

The following characters are typical:

1. The profile is more or less uniformly coloured throughout, with a darker humus-rich horizon on top.

2. pH is usually slightly acid and is never base-saturated.

3. Drainage varies from impeded to normal; it is rarely free.

4. Natural, i.e. uncultivated, brown earths occur typically under deciduous woodland in temperate climates. They are often developed over clays in this country. Fig. 5.

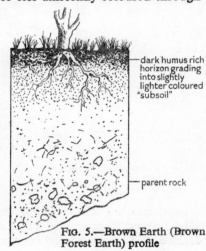

dark humus rich horizon grading into slightly lighter coloured "subsoil"

parent rock

3 decimetres

FIG. 5.—Brown Earth (Brown Forest Earth) profile

### iii. *Rendzinas*

Rendzinas are developed on basic rock such as Chalk, Carboniferous Limestone or Great Oolite. A single dark-coloured horizon is typical, but two distinct ones are often distinguishable, though the top may grade into the lower one. Fig. 6.

1. The upper horizon is usually dark brown, sometimes with a whitish tinge (especially on Chalk).

2. The profile grades into a lighter colour below and large and small fragments of the parent rock on which this horizon directly rests are distinguishable.

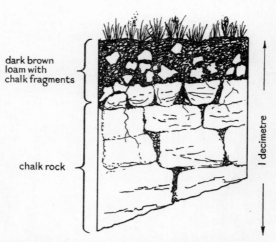

FIG. 6.—A Rendzina profile overlying Chalk rock

Rendzinas are often base-saturated (see p. 16) and have a pH of about 7 or above. They are usually shallow, freely drained, and carry a typical vegetation.

### iv. *Podsols*

Fig. 7 shows a typical podsol. Its sharply contrasted horizons are noticeable. These are:

1. A top layer chiefly humus ($A_0$ and $A_1$ horizons).
2. A characteristic ashy-grey (leached) horizon ($A_2$).
3. A dark band usually containing iron compounds with some humus ($B_1$ and $B_2$).
4. A lighter brown layer (C) grading into the rock below (D).

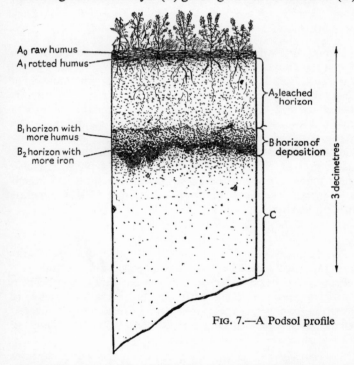

$A_0$ raw humus
$A_1$ rotted humus

$B_1$ horizon with more humus
$B_2$ horizon with more iron

$A_2$ leached horizon

B horizon of deposition

3 decimetres

C

FIG. 7.—A Podsol profile

Podsols are strongly acid with pH usually below 5·5, and drainage is excessive (see p. 15). They are developed on sandstones under conditions of moderately heavy rainfall.

Podsols are the typical soils of temperate climates where precipitation exceeds evaporation. On rocks and soils which allow solutions to percolate easily, the $A_2$ horizon becomes deficient in certain chemicals, notably bases, iron and aluminium compounds, through the leaching action of seeping solutions. The latter consists of a complex of humic acids and carbonic acid, formed from rain water which has taken up carbon dioxide from the air and from the decaying humus derived from the $A_0$ and $A_1$ horizons. Podsols therefore tend to be poor in some chemicals and are base-deficient. They carry heathland vegetation.

Though Brown Earths and Rendzinas are found in the temperate climatic zone they do not show typical Podsol characters. Rendzinas though often leached can maintain a basic condition because of the large reservoir of calcium carbonate derived from the parent rock. Drainage of Brown Earths does not usually allow seepage of solutions to the extent required for podsolisation. Basic substances, chiefly calcium carbonate, are often present, though the soil is not base-saturated. Thus in Brown Earths it is a physical factor which tends to prevent the development of a Podsol, whereas in Rendzinas chemical conditions counteract loss of minerals through leaching.

### v. *Peat*

Pedologically peat is a soil material and not a soil. Plants grow in it, and it will be treated as a special kind of soil.

Peat is the organic remains of plants (animals appear to contribute comparatively little to its formation). Due to anaerobic conditions these are partially decomposed. Peat is defined as a soil containing more than 65% by weight of organic material. It is classified as:

1. *Fen Peat* or *Alkaline Peat* in which the water contains basic substances dissolved from basic rocks either below, or from another area, and from which the natural drainage feeds into the fen peat.

2. *Acid Peat* is similar, but basic elements in the water are absent.

### vi. *Gley or Glei Soils* (*pronounced* "*glay*")

Certain soils especially in valleys or other low-lying areas are permanently waterlogged, almost to the surface. In this water-logged horizon the soil is usually greyish-green or greyish-blue (the gley horizon), and this may be taken as an indication of anaerobic conditions and the presence of organic matter. For a discussion of the chemical process involved in the formation of a gley horizon, reference should be made to the standard text-books (see p. 150).

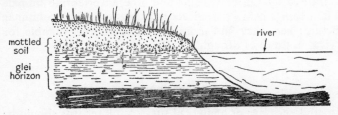

Fig. 8.—A rusty-brown mottled horizon overlying a glei horizon. This profile can often be seen in the banks of rivers and streams

A gley soil is often overlain by a horizon with characteristic rusty-brown mottling, fig. 8. This is a sign of impeded drainage, but not of a permanently waterlogged condition. The processes producing rusty markings are not fully understood, but they indicate the presence of oxidised iron compounds (see p. 15).

### vii. *Soil Structure*

The cracked appearance of the surface of a dried-out clay-soil and a crumbly impression of a lighter calcareous soil when dry, illustrate the meaning of soil structure, but must not be confused with texture.

The following classification of soil structure is useful for field biologists:

1. *Cubic*, in which the soil occurs in rough cubic units (fig. 9). If the cubes are large the structure is *cloddy*, if small it is *crumby*.

2. *Prismatic* or *Columnar* is shown in fig. 10. Each unit is elongated vertically.

3. *Laminated* structure shows elongation of each unit in one horizontal axis (fig.11).

4. *Polyhedral* (fig.12). The units each have an indefinite number of sides or may be *pyramidal*.

The natural structure of soil influences plants and animals living in and on it. Space between soil units allows air to penetrate easily. Ground beetles and other invertebrate animals can take refuge below the surface in a dryish soil with columnar structure; here they find more humid conditions suitable for survival in times of drought.


## V. SOIL RECORDING

In all descriptive or analytical surveys full records should be kept and soil maps made whenever possible. Profiles must be described accurately, the texture of at least the surface layers noted, and photographs—in black and white or colour, are useful. Samples of actual soils are invaluable for future comparisons and as records.

There are several ways in which specimen profiles can be kept. The one suggested here is particularly easy and quick to undertake. The profile is kept as a *monolith model*.

"Monolith" means a column, and a column of earth carefully dug out from the side of a pit or trench and enclosed in a long wooden box is one of the ways of keeping a profile record. This method takes much time and material, labour, and storage space. A model is therefore made by glueing a sample of each horizon of the profile on to a strip of wood, so that its appearance is similar to a column of the profile in the field.

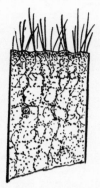

FIG. 9.—Cubic

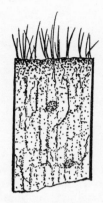

FIG. 10.—Prismatic or columnar

FIG. 11.—Laminated

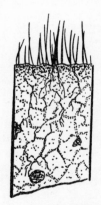

FIG. 12.—Polyhedral

SOIL STRUCTURE

## Materials Needed

1. The soil. Bag and label each horizon of the profile separately. A series of stout bags (not paper), each about $25 \times 35$ cm or $9 \times 14$ in. with string to close the neck is useful, and a number can be printed or stencilled on each.

In a field note-book enter the details of all horizons with the key numbers of the bags. Details of the site must be noted including geology, date, map-reference (see p. 140). Do this on the spot. Take samples of herbaceous vegetation, preferably the typical species, and any leaf litter lying on the surface of the profile.

2. Strips of wood 6 cm or $2\frac{1}{2}$ in. wide by about 8 mm or $\frac{3}{10}$ in. thick. Get a number of strips several feet long. Cut these to the lengths required. Most monoliths need about 30–40 cm or 12–16 in., but each should be calculated first (see below). Wood which does not warp is suitable. Unplaned timber is best as the rough surface acts as a key on to which the soil is stuck.

3. Carpenter's glue and a good-quality half-inch painter's brush (wash well in hot water after use!). Heat the glue with water till the solution is about the consistency of golden syrup.

## Method

Sandy and "light" soils should be dry and "heavy" clay soils moist (but not wet).

Choose a length of wood which allows all soil horizons and the notes to be glued on to it. Measure each horizon to *quarter scale* of that noted in the description of the profile in the field book. The notes are usually placed below the soil (see fig. 13).

It is necessary to visualise the profile as seen in the field; sketches are helpful. The horizons may not all have been of equal depth throughout so that they need not be marked parallel-sided on the wood. If the base of the lowest horizon was not seen (usually the underlying rock), slope it off towards the bottom in the same conventional way as in geological sections.

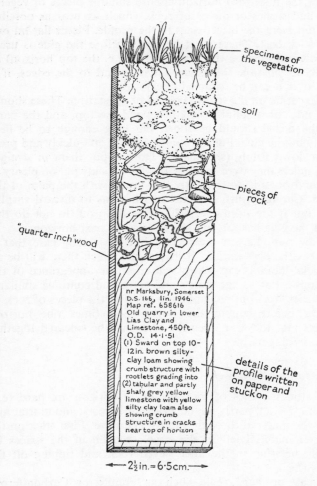

specimens of
the vegetation

soil

pieces of
rock

"quarter inch" wood

nr Marksbury, Somerset
D.S. 166, 1in. 1946.
Map ref. 658616
Old quarry in lower
Lias Clay and
Limestone, 450ft.
O.D. 14·1·51
(1) Sward on top 10-
12in. brown silty-
clay loam showing
crumb structure with
rootlets grading into
(2) tabular and partly
shaly grey yellow
limestone with yellow
silty clay loam also
showing crumb
structure in cracks
near top of horizon

details of the
profile written
on paper and
stuck on

◄— 2½in. = 6·5cm. —►

Fig. 13.—A soil monolith model

For the first (top) horizon choose suitable pieces of vegetation and stones or pieces of rock, which as near as possible will represent the larger ones in the profile. Pieces flat on one side stick best. These must be ready before the glue is used.

Now put glue on the first division (i.e. the top horizon) as evenly as possible. Make sure it is spread to the edges, if it runs over it can be trimmed afterwards.

Next stick on the selected pieces of vegetation. These should protrude for a suitable length beyond the top, and the parts on the board should be short, but long enough to be held firmly by the glue. Put the stones or rock on quickly and press them down firmly (see below). Do not put them in straight lines unless they were so in the profile. Quickly put on plenty of soil and press it down gently and firmly with the palm of the hand. Carefully turn over the board so as to discard surplus soil, but if the stones seem likely to drop off do not do this until the glue has set, but go on with the next horizon.

Now put glue on the second horizon taking care that it touches the first section. If it does not touch there will be an artificial-looking gap which will spoil the appearance of the monolith. Put on the stones and earth and continue similarly with each horizon, remembering to select the pieces of rock or stones before gluing the board. Sometimes one horizon grades into the next, then the two must be smeared together with the fingers.

*How to treat hard rock*

If stones, pieces of rock or the D horizon are hard (e.g. Chalk, Oolite), partly pound a piece in a pestle and mortar and pass the material through a fairly fine sieve. First stick on the coarser material left in the sieve, then fill in the spaces by gently pressing in the finer sieved rock and tipping off the surplus.

Break up hard rock, such as granite or Carboniferous Limestone, with a hammer and fit on the pieces like a jig-saw puzzle.

*Peat*

Stick on peat in sections about 1 cm or ¼ in. thick and big enough to overlap the board and each other; they shrink on drying.

*Clay soils*

These must be "puddled on" with the fingers to a thickness of about 5 mm or ⅕ in. finally wiping the surface with a moist rag to obliterate finger prints. Clay types of soil crack on drying and show their natural structure. If the cracks are very big, puddle in more clay; this usually sticks without the use of more glue. Such monoliths may take a few days to finish.

Do not throw away surplus soil and rock until it is certain the monolith is complete. It is useful to keep a store of spare material for renovations, especially of profiles collected in parts of the country which are not easily accessible.

Label the monolith with the following data which should be written or typed on good quality thick paper and glued on below the last horizon:

1. Name of place and county.
2. Ordnance Survey map number, scale and date of publication.
3. National grid reference (see p. 140).
4. Brief description of the type of exposure.
5. Height above sea-level O.D. (Ordnance Datum).
6. Date.

Monoliths are best transported wrapped separately in several folds of newspaper. They can be sprayed with various substances to make them more durable but are usually best without such treatment. Though they are fairly substantial they should be handled with care.

## Section C

# STUDIES OF PLANT LIFE

### I. How to Look at Vegetation

There are a number of different types of country in the British Isles. Apart from built-up areas, these are recognisable mainly by the vegetation. This may be planted, such as farmland and pine forest, or apparently natural like heathland, marsh or moorland. There are different kinds of "units" of vegetation some of which have familiar names—woodland, heathland, marsh and downland are examples. These are *plant communities*.

For the present purposes the following terms are used in describing and recording vegetation. These terms have not been defined consistently by all authors. Though differing slightly from Tansley (see p. 152) the aim of their present use for elementary purposes is simplicity and practicability.

*Plant Community*. A group of plants growing together recognisable as a distinct unit of vegetation. It may be any size.

*Plant Association*. A unit of vegetation within a plant community which is characterised by the presence of one species, the dominant (see p. 43), or several species (co-dominant species, see p. 43) after which the association is named.

The following illustrate the use of these terms: *Wet Oak Wood Community*—characterised by Oak *Quercus robur* L., Hazel *Corylus avellana* L., Bramble *Rubus* spp. (see p. 125), Honeysuckle *Lonicera periclymenum* L., Pendulous Sedge *Carex pendula* L., Wood Spurge *Euphorbia amygdaloides* L., Lesser Celandine *Ranunculus ficaria* L., Primrose *Primula vulgaris* Huds., Ground Ivy *Glechoma hederacea* L., Bugle *Ajuga reptans* L., and others. Within this community may be patches of Primroses together with a few other herbaceous plants; this. is a Primrose association. If this species and Ground Ivy are present in about equal proportions, i.e. they are co-dominant (p. 43) perhaps with a few other species this is called a Primrose–Ground Ivy Association. *Heathland Community—* Heather *Erica cinerea* L., Ling *Calluna vulgaris* L., Gorse *Ulex europaeus* L., Dwarf Furze *Ulex minor* Roth, Wavy Hair-grass *Deschampsia flexuosa* L., Bracken *Pteridium aquilinum* L., the moss *Hypnum schreberi* Brid. and other species are present.

These communities are distinguishable by the plants present. A few species may be common to both, but the majority often differ. Any number of associations make up a community.

It is worth completing the picture on a wider scale and defining *plant formation*, which the student, unless he has travelled abroad, is unable to appreciate. This term refers to the great belts of vegetation such as tropical forest, temperate forest, desert and tundra, which are governed by climate and altitude.

The plant formation embracing British vegetation is called *Deciduous Forest* with a small area of *Coniferous Forest* in the north of Scotland.

To describe British vegetation as Deciduous Forest may seem somewhat surprising since much of our land is not wooded. Nevertheless this would be the natural vegetation if man had not modified it to such a large extent in the interests of farming, forestry and amenities.

## II. SEMI-NATURAL VEGETATION

To find truly natural vegetation in Britain one must go to some of the remote parts of the Scottish Highlands, or to extensive areas of sand-dune. Even in such places man has often interfered in the natural course of events, for example, by cutting or planting trees, or by protection of deer and game, or in the case of sand-dunes by planting Marram Grass *Ammophila arenaria* L., or other stabilising vegetation. There is practically no natural vegetation in the British Isles today. A little is *semi-natural* but most is entirely artificial and man has been, and still is, the most important *biotic factor* (see p. 40) responsible for this. To the examples given may be added such *direct* interference as the burning of heathland, or *indirect* interference by protection, introduction or eradication of animals and plants. How would our vegetation have fared if the rabbit had not been introduced, it is believed, about the eleventh century?

Except for more drastic interference in certain parts of the country, such as drainage of wet areas, and extensive planting or felling of tracts of woodland, plant life may indicate the type of vegetation which would have been present under natural conditions. For example, much of our clay country still carries Oak forest with many of the associated characteristic plants. Limestone, including Chalk downland, often carries Beech *Fagus sylvatica* L., and Ash *Fraxinus excelsior* L., whereas Pine *Pinus sylvestris* L., and Birch *Betula verrucosa* Ehrh., are characteristic of acid and sandy heathland communities.

In areas which are largely cultivated, or where grassland for grazing is maintained, it is still often possible to trace plant associations which are characteristic of the types of soil and climatic conditions in which they occur. Such parts of the flora can only be remnants of what they were in former times before man brought about their modification.

The fact that the greater part of our vegetation is seminatural does not make it less worthy of study. There is as much to be gained by the study of a planted woodland as of the vegetation of a sand-dune or of the sea-shore. The structure of a planted wood is fundamentally the same as that of an area of natural forest.

## III. VEGETATION LAYERS

Almost every plant community or association whether natural, semi-natural or entirely artificial, has two or more distinct layers. The maximum number occurs in woodland (see p. 108). Here a *Bryophyte layer* (mostly mosses), a *field layer* of herbaceous plants, a *shrub* and a *tree layer* can be distinguished. These terms may be used in descriptive surveys of vegetation. Except for the trees which form the largest and most conspicuous layer, the flora and pattern of the other layers are in each case controlled by the presence and nature of the layer or layers above. This physiological relationship between the layers below that of the trees is often very intimate, as for example in a dense wood where much light is excluded by the shade cast from the tree and shrub layers, and where the ground flora layer consists of shade-tolerating species many of which are adapted to life in this habitat. The latter have such features as special food-storage organs, the capacity for early flowering and vegetative reproduction.

In Chalk sward too, at least two layers of vegetation are usually distinguishable, one of larger herbaceous plants below which is a layer of mosses largely dependent for its environment on the herbaceous plants. The same is true of open heathland where the heather layer shelters a moss and lichen flora under it.

Each layer has a different environment from the others. There are differences in air temperature, humidity, amount of light and shelter from wind. The same layer may differ in these respects from place to place, so that each layer itself may be thought of as a community made up of a number of associations.

So far only the aerial growth of plants has been discussed. But their rooting systems have equally important, if less readily observable, functions in the soil and upper parts of the rock. Root systems usually occur in layers, those of the larger plants often penetrating furthest into the soil (fig. 14). In this way competition for mineral nutrients and moisture is minimised. Because root systems grow in a three-dimensional pattern it is difficult to map them satisfactorily. The extent of a root system, and relationship of one system to another, can sometimes be seen in profiles, and can be recorded either photographically, or by drawing it to scale on graph paper.

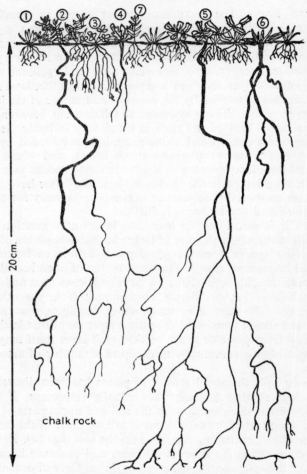

FIG. 14.—Root layers of Chalk down sward.
1. *Festuca ovina* (Sheep's Fescue). 2. *Galium verum* (Yellow Bedstraw). 3. *Trifolium pratense* (Clover). 4. *Cirsium acaule* (Stemless Thistle). 5. *Poterium sanguisorba* (Salad Burnet). 6. *Plantago lanceolata* (Ribwort). 7. *Linum catharticum* (Cathartic Flax)

## IV. PLANT SUCCESSION

When a piece of ground is dug and left it soon becomes covered with weeds. Chickweed *Stellaria media* L., Groundsel *Senecio vulgaris* L. and other plants as well as grasses grow. If the ground is left larger plants appear, and after several years brambles, shrubs and young trees become established. There has been a qualitative change of the vegetation. It has altered through the disappearance of some species and the appearance of others.

Different "stages" of vegetation can be seen almost anywhere. *Herbaceous vegetation* is "invaded" by small bushes (*scrub*) and scrub by trees (*woodland*). When mature, woodland may be very dense (*closed canopy*, see p. 108).

This change from smaller to larger species ending in woodland is called *plant succession*. In the semi-natural vegetation of this country, the true beginning of plant succession is rarely seen (see p. 35), except in quarries, or where a land slip has occurred. As the rock weathers and humus from decaying lichens becomes mixed with it, as well as moisture and air, a shallow soil is formed. Other plants become established, for example, mosses if the habitat is moist enough, and later those species characteristic of the soil and climate. The succession now leaves the stage of *primary colonisation*, and enters the *sward stage* in which herbaceous plants, including grasses, make up the bulk of the vegetation.

In Great Britain semi-natural herbaceous vegetation is often the beginning of plant succession on bare ground, or artificially exposed rock surfaces.

If the succession is not more or less permanently modified, i.e. if it is not *deflected* by the influence of grazing animals—rabbits or sheep for example—it passes gradually into the *scrub stage* in which shrubs predominate. Much Chalk downland in southern England is covered with Hawthorn *Crataegus monogyna* Jacq. or Dogwood *Cornus sanguinea* L. scrub, interspersed with other species like Wayfaring Tree *Viburnum lantana* L. and Wild Privet *Ligustrum vulgare* L.

In certain areas, notably the South Downs of Sussex, and parts of the Pennines, sheep-grazing has been practised for many centuries, and as long as the animals nibbled and trod the sward, shrubs and trees were unable to become established. When recently the industry declined, coarser species of herbs appeared, and seedlings of shrubs and trees were able to grow. The succession, formerly deflected, is now moving forward again. This change can be seen in a number of places, though it is only a few decades since sheep grazed on them. Scrub is rapidly invading what was once good pasture, and the first suggestion of the final stage of succession, that of woodland, can sometimes be recognised by the presence of young trees. Sheep are here a biotic factor (see p. 36).

Scrub gradually passes over into *woodland*—the end or *climax* of succession. This may undergo several changes. Thus Beech may succeed Ash, because Ashes do not cast much shade, and Beech Trees are able to grow up through them and finally dominate the community. The climax is therefore Beech Wood and Ash Wood is the *sub-climax* phase.

More or less permanent deflection of plant succession occurs where fires periodically devastate heathland, and prevent growth of scrub and woodland. In a sense deflection is caused by climate and altitude. In some of the higher and wetter areas of northern England, and parts of Scotland, woodland is unable to develop under the unfavourable climatic conditions, and the climax vegetation is often open moorland with Ling, Heather and Purple Moor-grass *Molinia coerulea* L. associations predominating.

Plant succession is taking place everywhere, and different phases, one imperceptibly passing into another, can be seen in semi-natural and entirely artificial vegetation.

A phase in plant succession is called a *seral stage* or *seral community*. A *sere* is a complete example of succession. If this takes place on dry land, as the development of woodland on Chalk Downs, it is called a *xerosere*.

A *hydrosere* is the development of woodland from open water. A pond or lake ultimately becomes filled in, through the accumulation of plant débris on the bottom, under more or less anaerobic conditions where it does not rot. This usually takes place from the edges and is often mixed with silt and mud. Over a long period the accumulations replace the water, and dry land on which terrestrial plants grow is formed. From this stage the succession develops to climax woodland.

In Great Britain the majority of seres are *secondary*. That is, they have developed on soil already formed, or in water in which the succession has been artificially deflected. *Primary seres* are found only on areas which have not before carried vegetation—artificially disturbed ground, newly made water habitats, etc.

To some extent the soil of secondary seres is "second hand". It is ready-made and possesses some of the characters originating from the influence of a former vegetation cover. This is a reminder that not only does the soil influence the plants, but that plants can, and do, modify the soil in which they grow.

Vegetation can be analysed into orderly units of space (the study of formations, communities and associations) and of time (plant succession). In the next section methods of studying and recording vegetation are discussed.

Hitherto only the names of a few of the more familiar plants have been mentioned. Before any serious study of vegetation is contemplated, reasonable proficiency in identification must be acquired. Knowledge of the use of a flora is indispensable and at least the commoner species in groups other than the flowering plants must be learnt. In a detailed survey it is often necessary to call in the help of specialists dealing with the more critical groups, such as Bryophytes and Lichens, and the more difficult families, genera and species of flowering plants. It cannot be too strongly stressed that practice in the use of keys, and correct identification of specimens by whatever means, is a very necessary preliminary to plant study in the field.

## V. RECORDING VEGETATION

### i. *Introduction*

Precise information, qualitative and quantitative, about plant communities and associations is often needed for comparison, and a description of the same community, at different times of the year, may be wanted to show the effects of seasonal changes; the effect of application of fertilisers, weed killers, or the influence of grazing animals also demand this information. Succession can be studied by recording vegetation in consecutive years. The effect of denuding a small area of plants and watching recolonisation requires accurate recording of the plants from time to time (p. 103). The zoologist needs a vegetation map as a basis for his work.

THE DIFFERENT METHODS OF RECORDING VEGETATION ARE USED ONLY FOR THE SPECIFIC PURPOSE OF ILLUSTRATING A FEATURE OR FEATURES OF VEGETATION. AS MERE EXERCISES THEY ARE USELESS AND A LABORIOUS WASTE OF TIME.

Make a preliminary inspection of the vegetation first, note the more important features and the places where these are best seen, then decide what is to be recorded and the methods to be used. Vegetation is recorded qualitatively or quantitatively.

### ii. *Qualitative Recording*

#### (a) *Listing*

In making a list of the species of a vegetation unit it is desirable to record the relative importance of each species. This gives a rough idea of the contribution which each makes to the community or association.

The following notations are useful:

| | | | |
|---|---|---|---|
| $d$ = dominant | | $o$ = occasional | |
| $a$ = abundant | | $r$ = rare | |
| $f$ = frequent | | $vr$ = very rare | |

*Dominant* does not necessarily mean the most numerous species. A dominant plant is one which, if removed from vegetation, would visibly alter its appearance. The species which contributes most in bulk either by reason of its size or numbers (or both), is the dominant; it is the species which has the greatest physiological effect on the environment. If two or more species contribute equally they are *co-dominant*.

*Abundant, frequent, occasional* and *rare* are terms used for describing relative numerical relationships.

*Locally* (*l*) is prefixed only to dominant, abundant and frequent. It indicates the relative prevalence of a species (or several species) which forms (or form) a major feature in one or more patches in the community.

(b) *The Grid Map*

Vegetation can be recorded on the 25-in., 6-in. or $2\frac{1}{2}$-in. map by shading, colouring or by the use of symbols. But for smaller areas the grid map is used. This is made as follows:

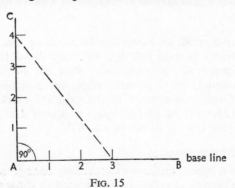

FIG. 15

1. Peg out a base line (see fig. 15). It is best to make this one side of a rectangle enclosing the area to be studied. Surveyor's levelling poles painted black, white and red, are useful, but bushes, trees or a fence can be used.

2. Divide the base line into equal parts according to the number of surveyors. For example, if the base line is 30 metres

and there are ten surveyors, then 3 metres would be a suitable interval.

3. Starting from one end of the base line set out other lines (*offsets*) at right angles to the base at 3-metre intervals. Construct a triangle on the base line *AB*. Make that side of the triangle which lies in the base line 3 units long, and the offset *AC* 4 units. When the distance between *B* and *C* is 5 units the angle *CAB* is 90° (see fig. 15).

4. Choose a series of suitable symbols for the different units of vegetation. In any case this will have to be done afterwards back in the laboratory, when a single map, preferably coloured, is constructed on squared paper from the strip records.

5. The observers then map each strip on squared paper or on a map previously obtained for the purpose.

6. Determine the correct orientation of the base line or of the whole area by compass and give the grid reference, scale and other necessary data.

Fig. 16 is a grid map of vegetation of a pond near Priddy in Somerset.

To map a small area one square metre or less, the quadrat or grid frame is used (see fig. 19). Lay down the grid on a selected patch of the vegetation. Plot the position of each plant accurately on to squared paper using symbols or initial letters. If the four corners of the grid are marked by small pegs, the area can be plotted again at a later date and changes in vegetation can be shown (see p. 47).

## (c) *The Profile Transect*

This is a quick method of recording change of vegetation from one type to another. It can be used to show the influence of different soils on plants, and other factors affecting their distribution (slope, waterlogging, trampling, etc.).

1. Stretch a tape or rope marked at suitable intervals, preferably in the metric system, across the types of vegetation to be studied. Make certain that this is done at a suitable place where the features to be recorded are most obvious.

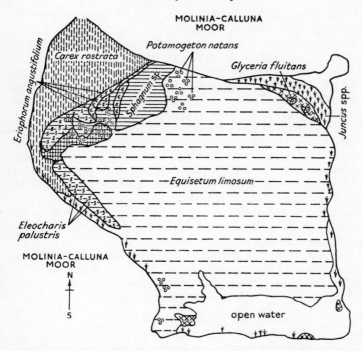

MOLINIA-CALLUNA
MOOR

*Potamogeton natans*

*Carex rostrata*

*Glyceria fluitans*

*Eriophorum angustifolium*

*Sphagnum sp.*

*Juncus spp.*

*Equisetum limosum*

*Eleocharis palustris*

MOLINIA-CALLUNA
MOOR

N

S

open water

FIG. 16.—Grid map of vegetation of a pond near Priddy, Somerset

2. First record topographical features in profile form. For this squared paper is useful, though the information can be recorded in the field note-book and later transferred to squared paper. If topography shows little variation, judge the profile by eye. But if there are steep slopes, gauge the exact profile in this way.

3. Place a spirit-level fitted with sights at the lowest end of the line. Measure the height of the sights from the ground. Another person must walk along the line with a measuring staff, and stop at any convenient interval, to allow a sighting

to be made on the staff. The point of intersection of the sighting line is determined on the staff by the person holding it moving his finger up and down. Record the distance of the point of intersection from the ground. Repeat this until the whole of the profile has been plotted. At the end of each reading the spirit-level is brought up to the point where a reading has just been made. This method is best where the slope is not too steep.

When steep slopes are involved, a preferable method is to start at the highest point, and run out a marked line to any convenient distance, keeping it horizontal by means of a spirit-level. At any point the height from the ground is noted at which the line intersects a measuring pole, and this is plotted on graph paper. Repeat this until the whole of the line has been covered. If no spirit-level is available, a third person can usually gauge the level of the line sufficiently accurately by eye from one side and well away from it.

4. Now divide the line into sections according to the number of observers. Each person makes a list of the plants, with their approximate heights, in his or her section. It is rarely necessary to record every plant. A convenient spacing is:

Open sward—every decimetre (10 cm).
Heathland—every half-metre.
Scrub—every metre, or greater intervals on a long line.

Record only those plants actually crossed by the line—above and below—and note the height and extent of overhanging boughs.

5. Record any change of soil, pH, the presence of paths or other tracks.

6. Determine the position of the transect on the map and give a grid reference for it (see p. 140).

7. In the laboratory plot the transect profile to a suitable scale on squared paper. The vertical height is usually exaggerated, unless the transect was taken over slopes or down a steep hillside. Draw in the plants to scale using suitable symbols. Show shade cast by boughs and branches as a thick black line

of correct length, and at the right height above the profile. If it is impossible to put a bough in the right position above the profile the correct height must be indicated in figures.

8. Include all essential data—title, locality, vertical and horizontal scale, symbols, names of surveyors, etc.

Fig. 17 shows a profile transect of vegetation at the edge of a pond.

### (d) *The Belt Transect*

This is a useful method for recording colonisation of a bare piece of ground, such as a newly-made bank, or the rapid change from one type of vegetation to another where a line transect does not cover enough of the plants to show this.

1. Peg out two parallel lines across the area to be mapped; the distance between the lines must be varied according to the vegetation.

2. Choose appropriate symbols and map the vegetation between these lines section by section, e.g. a square metre at a time.

3. Use squared paper, and back in the laboratory make a fair copy which can later preferably be coloured.

4. Keep a record of the scale and location of the transect and put these on the final copy.

Fig. 17 is a belt transect across a path in Chalkland sward.

### iii. *Quantitative Recording*

As in qualitative sampling (see p. 44) the grid frame is used for recording vegetation in which the plants are small (see below). For large areas, including shrubs and trees, grid samples are not suitable, and an accurate assessment of the vegetation can usually be made by a direct count of the bigger plants, recording the number per unit area, and restricting the grid frame counts to the herbaceous part of the vegetation.

### (a) *The Quadrat or Grid Frame*

This is a right-angled frame made from metal, or pegged out with string on the ground. Many plants tend to grow in a

5

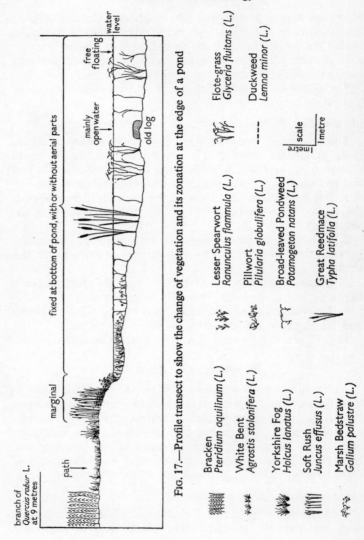

FIG. 17.—Profile transect to show the change of vegetation and its zonation at the edge of a pond

Bracken
*Pteridium aquilinum* (L.)

White Bent
*Agrostis stolonifera* (L.)

Yorkshire Fog
*Holcus lanatus* (L.)

Soft Rush
*Juncus effusus* (L.)

Marsh Bedstraw
*Galium palustre* (L.)

Lesser Spearwort
*Ranunculus flammula* (L.)

Pillwort
*Pilularia globulifera* (L.)

Broad-leaved Pondweed
*Potamogeton natans* (L.)

Great Reedmace
*Typha latifolia* (L.)

Flote-grass
*Glyceria fluitans* (L.)

Duckweed
*Lemna minor* (L.)

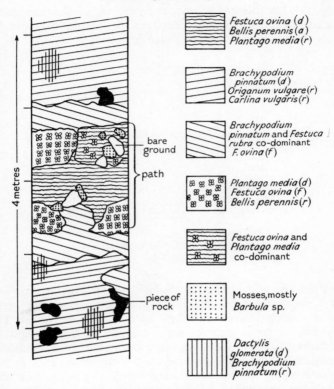

Festuca ovina (*d*)
Bellis perennis (*a*)
Plantago media (*r*)

Brachypodium
pinnatum (*d*)
Origanum vulgare (*r*)
Carlina vulgaris (*r*)

Brachypodium
pinnatum and Festuca
rubra co-dominant
F. ovina (*f*)

Plantago media (*d*)
Festuca ovina (*f*)
Bellis perennis (*r*)

Festuca ovina and
Plantago media
co-dominant

Mosses, mostly
Barbula sp.

Dactylis
glomerata (*d*)
Brachypodium
pinnatum (*r*)

bare
ground

path

piece of
rock

4 metres

FIG. 18.—Belt transect across a path in a field to show the effect of regular trampling on the vegetation. Only the major species in each association are shown. (See p. 42, ii (*a*))

clump. A square frame would cover this but probably not the surrounding species. A rectangle is more likely to cover the clump *and* the surrounding species and is therefore preferable to a square. A frame with an area of 0·25 sq. metre is useful. It is usual to divide the frame into smaller areas by cross-pieces either fixed or adjusted so as to slide along the sides (fig. 19). The quadrat is used for comparing plant communities or associations either quantitatively or qualitatively and for recording seasonal and other changes in plant life.

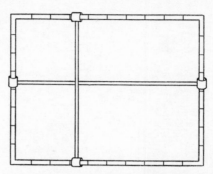

FIG. 19.—A grid frame. Any convenient scale can be used. The cross arms are movable

Place the grid *at random within the same plant association*. If, when the frame is cast it lands on a feature which is not part of the vegetation, e.g. a rabbit hole, it must be recast. The number of samples for effective comparison will depend on the area. Generally speaking larger areas need about a hundred samples, but in smaller ones twenty-five counts are enough. No exact number can be stated, only statistical analysis of a trial and error sampling could give an accurate figure, but the above will serve as a guide. The size of the sample can be determined by the following method:

Make a list of the number of species of plant in any area within the unit to be sampled beginning with a fairly small frame *ABBB* (fig. 20).

Without changing the position of the frame count the number of species in a larger area *ACCC*. Repeat this a number of times increasing the area by geometrical progression at each count, *ADDD*, *AEEE*, etc.

Now plot the readings for the number of species of each count against the size of each sample area (fig. 21).

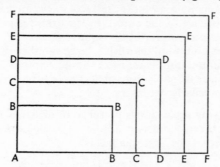

FIG. 20.—Determination of optimum sample size in sward. (See p. 50)

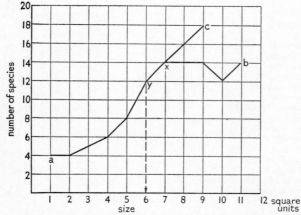

FIG. 21.—Graph of determination of sample size in sward. For explanation see text

The curve *ab* should fall off at a point *x* which represents the maximum area needed to include all species. In practice the curve usually follows the line *ac*. This is due to a number of casual species which are often present scattered throughout the community. Determination of the size of the sample unit is therefore taken at a point $y$ halfway between zero and the maximum distance of the curve. In the example given the size of the sample unit would be six square units.

In complex communities with a large number of species the trial for minimum sample unit size should be repeated a number of times, till a reasonably consistent figure is recorded. At least ten trials are usually necessary.

The following table shows presence or absence in a series of grid counts taken from two adjoining associations and illustrates one use of the grid quadrat.

| | Rough sward | | | | | Path | | | | | Rough sward | | | | |
|---|---|---|---|---|---|---|---|---|---|---|---|---|---|---|---|
| | 1 | 2 | 3 | 4 | 5 | 1 | 2 | 3 | 4 | 5 | 1 | 2 | 3 | 4 | 5 |
| *Bellis perennis* L. (Daisy) | | | | | | | | | | | | | | | |
| *Brachypodium pinnatum* (L.) (Tor Grass) | | | | | | | | | | | | | | | |
| *Festuca ovina* L. (Sheep's Fescue) | | | | | | | | | | | | | | | |
| *Helianthemum chamaecistus* Mill. (Rock Rose) | | | | | | | | | | | | | | | |
| *Hieraceum pilosella* L. (Mouse-ear Hawkweed) | | | | | | | | | | | | | | | |
| *Plantago lanceolata* L. (Ribwort) | | | | | | | | | | | | | | | |
| *P. media* L. (Hoary Plantain) | | | | | | | | | | | | | | | |
| *Poa annua* L. (Annual Meadow Grass) | | | | | | | | | | | | | | | |
| *Poterium sanguisorba* L. (Salad Burnet) | | | | | | | | | | | | | | | |

The effects of trampling on the path and apparent elimination of some species through competition in the rough sward association in this Chalk down community can be seen from this table. A grid frame of 4 sq. decimetres was used. A total of 15 trials, five on each side of the path and five in the path, was made; each sample was taken at random. Presence or absence was recorded irrespective of the number of each species in each sample area.

## (b) *Percentage Occurrence or Valence Analysis*

Record the number of times in which a species occurs in at least one hundred samples, and express this as a percentage of the total number of samples. Small samples are usually adequate. This is also a measure of constancy, and indicates whether or not a species is well distributed and of constant occurrence. It is useful for showing the change of composition of different vegetation types, and if the samples are taken down a transect line, e.g. through the zones at the edge of a pond, the percentage occurrence can be shown at the appropriate points on the profile.

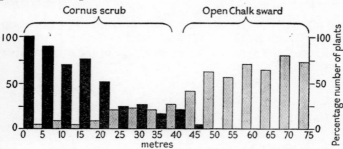

FIG. 22.—Histogram of the percentage occurrence of *Mercurialis perennis* (black) and *Festuca ovina* tufts (dotted) along a transect showing transition from *Cornus sanguinea* scrub to open Chalk sward. Two sample counts each 1 sq. m and separated by 1 m distance were taken at random at 10 m intervals between the points 0—75 m . . . 15 m. The unmarked portion of each column represents other species or bare ground. The shade preference of *M. perennis* is clearly shown and *F. ovina* becomes dominant in the sward

## (c) *The Composition of the Vegetation*

This can be shown from the results of a valence analysis in the following way:

The percentage number of occurrences are divided into five groups:

Group *I*  0–20%    Group *II*  21–40%    Group *III*  41–60%
,,  *IV*  61–80%    ,,    *V*  81–100%

for example,

Group

*F. ovina* (Sheep's Fescue) 95%, i.e. it occurs 95 times
out of 100 samples . . . . . . *V*
*B. erectus* (Upright Brome-grass) 26% . . . *II*
*B. sylvaticum* (Soft False Brome-grass) 22% . . *II*
*V. hirta* (Hairy Violet) 19% . . . . . *I*
*B. perfoliata* (Yellow-wort) 2% . . . . *I*
*O. vulgare* (Marjoram) 46% . . . . . *III*
*L. catharticum* (Cathartic Flax) 65% . . . *IV*
*T. drucei* (Druce's Thyme) 7% . . . . *I*
*C. flacca* (Glaucous Sedge) 4% . . . . *I*
*B. purum* (a moss) 8% . . . . . . *I*

Of a total of ten species only 1 falls in Group *V*, 1 in Group
*IV*, 1 in Group *III*, 2 in Group *II* and 5 in Group *I*.

Each group is expressed as a percentage of the total number
of species:

$$\frac{\text{No. of Species in group}}{\text{Total no. of species}} \times 100$$

e.g. from the above:

Group *I* = 50     Group *II* = 10     Group *III* = 10
Group *IV* = 20     Group *V* = 10

From this a histogram is constructed, fig. 23. This gives a
characteristic J-shaped figure. The long limb of the "J" is the
large number of occasional species, and the others represent
the dominant or sub-dominant species in the community.

(d) *Plant Cover*

*Cover Index* of the species in herbaceous vegetation is in part
a measure of their success, as well as a record of the structure
of the vegetation. Two ways of studying plant cover are given.

1. *Visual Cover Index*. Here the quadrat grid is used. Estimate by eye the percentage area covered by the species in each
small square of the grid. Record in tenths (i.e. $\frac{10}{10} = 100\%$).
This is an easier working figure and can be converted into a
percentage afterwards. Tabulate the results either in column
form, or as a block histogram. The number of samples will

depend on the vegetation, and is determined by the method described on p. 50, unless only selected species are being recorded.

2. *Point Cover Index.* Ten knitting needles or skewers, all the same length, are suspended through a piece of wood; each is separated from its neighbour by about 2 cm or $\frac{3}{4}$ in.—or more in very coarse vegetation. Hold the apparatus *at random* over the vegetation, and lower it until the ends of the needles touch the plants. Identify and record each species, i.e. ten readings per frame, and at least twenty separate frames must be done—a total of two hundred points. Each species is 100% cover at the point touched by a needle. Add up the total number of touches for each species and express it as a percentage of the total points (200 or more). Count bare ground but *subtract* each point from the total number of species of plants.

If the vegetation is obviously layered, for example when mosses and liverworts are present below the sward plants, regard the layers as separate communities and make separate analyses for each.

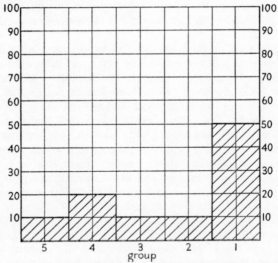

FIG. 23.—Histogram of composition of vegetation

## Section D

# THE STUDY OF ANIMALS IN THE FIELD

## I. Introduction

Animals, unlike most plants, are capable of movement from one place to another. This makes their study entirely different, other methods are necessary for collecting and counting them, and more than one method may have to be used for the study of the same species in different stages of its life. Insects comprise about three-quarters of all known animals. All except a few primitive insects undergo a series of changes or *metamorphoses* and may be found in the field as egg (*ovum*), caterpillar (*larva*), chrysalis (*pupa*) or perfect insect (*imagine*) according to the season.

Animals feed on complex substances already elaborated by plants from simpler materials. The variety of life in the animal kingdom is astonishing; there are few habitats which animals have not been able to colonise. Some live on the ground, some in it; fresh water, brackish water and the sea are inhabited by different species. Some have conquered the air, and many have become intimately associated with man and his activities.

*Herbivorous* animals feed on plants, others—the *carnivores* —are exclusively flesh eaters. The *omnivores* live on a mixed diet, and *scavengers* may be included amongst this group.

Those animals which attack and prey on other animals are *predators*. Others, the *parasites*, go about this in a more subtle way; they do not immediately kill their prey, but sooner or later it usually dies as a result of their activities. Parasites are closely associated with their hosts and are usually highly specialised. Parasites may be parasitised themselves by *hyper-*

*parasites* and these again may be attacked by *hyper-hyper-parasites*. There are degrees of parasitism—partial parasites or *parasitoids*, for example the parasitic Hymenoptera which are free living for part of their lives.

These are only a few examples illustrating the variety of animal life. For various reasons, not the least being the greater number of animal species, Field Zoology is less advanced than Botany.

## II. Niches, Food Chains and the Pyramid of Numbers

Plants form the basis of food for all animals, and there is a direct relationship between the plant and the herbivore which feeds on it, and again between the carnivore and the herbivore on which it preys. This is a *food-chain*, and there are rarely more than four or five links, though cross-links often occur as is illustrated by the following diagram.

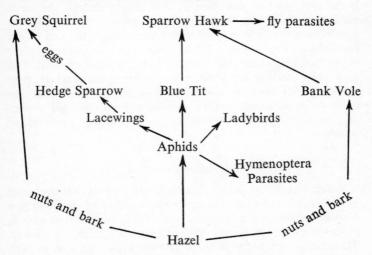

A simple food-chain of part of the fauna in a mixed deciduous wood in the Weald, Surrey, 1952.

The term *niche* refers to the livelihood of an animal. Elton (p. 153) has aptly compared a niche to a trade or profession in human society; it is the means whereby an animal gets its food. The niche is determined by the nature of the food and the latter is related to the size of the animal. Thus in the carnivores of a woodland community there is the predator niche occupied by foxes, badgers, stoats and weasels among mammals, and hawks and tawny owls (day and night feeders respectively) among birds. Other carnivore niches are the shrews which feed on invertebrates, and birds which feed on aphids and other insects. These niches are distinguished by the size and different food requirements of the predators. Similar niches occur amongst herbivores, scavengers and omnivores.

From the food-chain diagram there is clearly a larger number of the smaller animals on which the bigger ones prey. Excepting parasites, this is a universal rule, and is called the *Pyramid of Numbers*. The smaller herbivores or scavengers reproduce at a faster rate, and so maintain their numbers despite the large predators which feed on them. The predators, because of their greater size, reproduce more slowly and occupy the end of the food-chain. From this it follows that most predators, unlike many herbivores, are not restricted to one kind of food, and that their territorial systems are often well-marked thus ensuring that they do not come into competition with one another for the same food. Food-chains of parasites get smaller and smaller and thus comform to a reversed pyramid of numbers.

### III. IDENTIFICATION

When identifying plants there is usually a reasonable chance of being able to name to the species a number of the flowering plants, conifers, ferns and the rest. With animals the case is different, especially for the zoologist with little field experience. There are a number of difficult or "specialist" groups, in each of which an expert is needed to undertake competent identification down to the species. The mites (Acarina) and Ichneumons of the Hymenoptera are examples. But this must not discourage the beginner. The relationship of a species, say of insect, to the host plant or to other creatures and to its surroundings can often be determined without precise reference to its name, though there are obvious advantages in knowing the name. It is fortunate that some groups in which the members are taxonomically related often have similar habits. For example, all aphids, or green flies, feed on the sap of plants, and all dragonfly larvae are aquatic and active predators feeding on other creatures in the water.

Much useful work can be done in the field with little experience in animal identification. It is best to begin with the broader outlines of classification and not to worry about identification to the species (see p. 122), though a few groups like birds, mammals, some butterflies and moths may not present much difficulty. Good museum collections of accurately named specimens are invaluable, so too is an adequate reference library. If millipedes (Diplopoda) can be distinguished from centipedes (Chilopoda), spiders (Araneida) from harvest-spiders (Opiliones) and so on, this knowledge can be of great help in less advanced field work. Unidentified specimens can be preserved (see p. 133) and later sent to a specialist for identification (see p. 145).

## IV. APPARATUS AND METHODS FOR ANIMAL STUDY

Animals occur in every habitat. There is much variation in the method and apparatus used for their capture, for instance, in the shape, kind of material and colour of a kite net, or the use of different baits, but the principles involved are relatively few and are described here.

The different pieces of apparatus are designed to exploit specific habitats in order to get accurate qualitative, and sometimes quantitative, data of the fauna. If the wrong apparatus is used it is impossible to make an accurate assessment of the population, time will be wasted, and the apparatus is likely to be damaged.

Summary of more important apparatus

1. *For catching flying insects—kite net.*
2. *For finding insects, etc., on herbage—sweep net.*
3. *For catching insects, etc., in water—water net, diatom or plankton net, trawl net.*
4. *For finding insects, spiders, etc., on the branches of bushes and trees—beating tray.*
5. *Collecting from moss, leaf litter, etc.—sieve, sorting table, Berlèse or Tüllgren funnel.*
6. *Extracting animals from soil—flotation, heat.*
7. *Traps, attrahent substances, the use of chemicals.*

### i. *Nets*

There are three main types with much variation in shape, size and material.

### (a) *Kite net*

This is essentially a light-weight frame with a bag of mosquito netting or similar material, preferably dark green or black. A white bag should never be used; it appears to be conspicuous to some insects, and at night when a torch is used, moths are difficult to see in it. The bag should be rounded, not pointed at the bottom, and long enough to allow it to be folded over to retain an insect. Trapping insects on the ground under the net should be avoided. When about to use the net, hold the end of the bag in the left hand until the net is actually brought into action. An insect can be disturbed by the movement of the net as it is

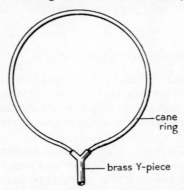

FIG. 24.—Kite net frame made of cane; the net can be of any convenient width but is usually about 3 decimeters (1 ft)

released from the left hand, and swept towards the creature catching it as it flies off (see fig. 24).

There are various makes of kite net. Some have a ring of flexible metal which allows the net to be folded by a twisting action. Others can be taken to pieces.

The kite net should only be used for catching insects on the wing. The killing bottle or collecting tins can be opened and used inside the net bag. A handle makes the net less easy to wield and is rarely necessary.

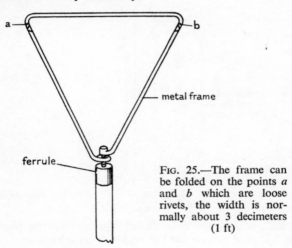

FIG. 25.—The frame can be folded on the points *a* and *b* which are loose rivets, the width is normally about 3 decimeters (1 ft)

## (b) *Sweep net*

This net is used for collecting insects, spiders, etc., from herbaceous plants. It consists of a heavy triangular frame to which is attached a bag made of strong closely woven material such as calico. The colour is unimportant. The depth of the bag need not be as much as in the kite net and the bottom should be rounded. It may be attached directly on to the frame or to it by means of metal rings. The latter prevent wear and tear on the rim of the net-bag. The frame can be rounded and of stout cane, but a metal triangular frame in preferable, fig. 25.

The net, with a short wooden handle if preferred, is swept to and fro in front of the operator. The front edge of the frame jars the plants and the displaced insects fall into the bag and are put into a killing bottle or collected through an aspirator, (fig. 26). The front edge of the net must be kept parallel with

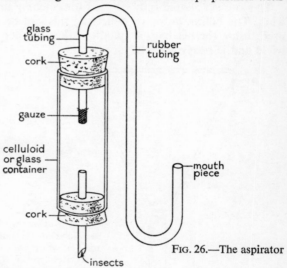

glass tubing

rubber tubing

cork

gauze

celluloid or glass container

cork

mouth piece

insects

Fig. 26.—The aspirator

the ground, and steady determined sweeps must be used. A sweep net should not be used in water or as a kite net.

(c) *Water nets*

1. *Dredge nets:* there is much variation in size of the frame as well as the material used. A useful shape has the same frame as the sweep net (fig. 25). The triangular shape allows the bottom of the pond or river to be scraped. The bag must be made of material which lets through fine sand but not animals visible to the naked eye, and it must be strong and must not rot easily. Bolting silk is recommended. A handle is necessary and a screw-on attachment to the ferrule is recommended (fig. 27). Moderately fast to-and-fro sweeps are best.

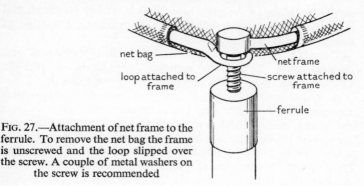

Fig. 27.—Attachment of net frame to the ferrule. To remove the net bag the frame is unscrewed and the loop slipped over the screw. A couple of metal washers on the screw is recommended

2. *Diatom or plankton net* (fig. 28). This is a small net with a circular cane or stout wire frame about 15 cm (6 in.) in diameter. The bag, made of very closely woven material such as nylon, is tapered to a point through which a rimmed glass tube is attached. Alternatively, a metal tube with a thread which screws into a ring attached to the tapered end of the net, can

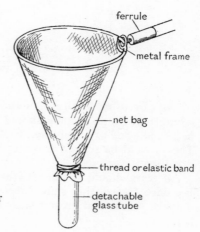

Fig. 28.—Diatom net; diameter 10 cm or 4 in.

be used in place of the glass tube. This is readily removed, and if a series of such tubes (with corks) is available, a number of samples can be kept separate.

The plankton net is used for collecting small organisms and concentrating them into samples. Ostracods, Copepods, Diatoms and other microscopic life are taken this way.

3. *Trawl net:* this has a large net bag made of similar material to the dredge net, but is usually made of a coarser mesh. It is conical, and is attached to a wide circular or stout triangular frame. The net is trawled by means of a rope from a boat, or by two people on opposite banks of a stream. The frame must be stout metal with appropriate attachments for the rope (fig. 29). Large animals, fish, amphibia, etc., are caught with the trawl net, and bigger samples are taken than with the dredge net.

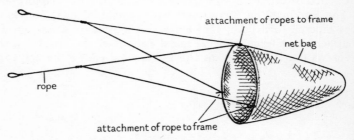

FIG. 29.—A trawl net; diameter 1 m or 3 ft

*The care of nets.* All nets should be dried on return to the laboratory. On no account should any net, especially the water net, be allowed to remain wet. New kite net bags are often stiff. They should be soaked in water for a few minutes and then dried ready for use.

All tears should be mended as soon as possible. If a rim becomes frayed this should be attended to before further damage results and greater wear occurs to other parts of the net.

## ii. *Beating tray*

This is a piece of cloth, preferably black or dark green, but never white, stretched on a light-weight frame. It is held under branches of trees and shrubs which are then beaten with a stick. Insects, spiders, etc., are dislodged and fall on to the tray, from which they are collected into tubes or through an aspirator (fig. 30).

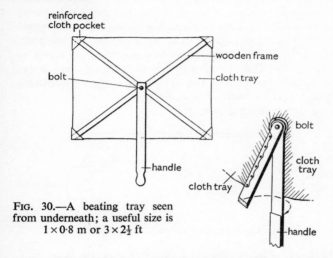

Fig. 30.—A beating tray seen from underneath; a useful size is $1 \times 0.8$ m or $3 \times 2\frac{1}{2}$ ft

The apparatus should be made so that it can be folded and it should have a short handle by which to hold it. The Bignell type of beating tray is very useful, but a sheet, a piece of newspaper or an umbrella can also be used. When tapping the branches give sharp raps on the main part, so that the whole branch is jarred and the foliage is not damaged.

### iii. *Collecting from moss, leaf-litter, etc.*

A great variety of invertebrate animals lives in woodland litter, piles of loose moss, and moss growing on the ground, accumulated leaves and flotsam brought down by rivers in flood and in other accumulated material. It is not always easy to find the animals by looking in these habitats without using the methods given in the following sections.

Such material can be examined on a piece of white water-proof cloth in the field. A small open mesh sieve may be helpful.

An easier method is to bring sacks of the material back to the laboratory. A sieve with about four holes to a square inch is used to sort small quantities of the débris on to a white-topped table, or on to a piece of white material. A 100-watt electric light bulb is suspended about ten inches above the centre of the table. If a special table can be set aside for this purpose, strips of half-inch square wood can be nailed to its edges as shown in fig. 31. The sorted débris is swept away into a bin through the gap between *A* and *B*. The edging stops animals from falling over the sides. The table is improved by a coat of high-gloss light-coloured paint.

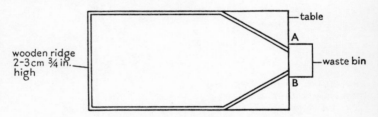

Fig. 31.—Plan of table for sorting leaf litter, etc. A convenient size is 16 dm × 8 dm or $5\frac{1}{2} \times 2\frac{1}{2}$ ft

Most of the animals in moss, woodland litter, etc., are negatively phototactic and move away from the bright light. They are also activated by the heat from the bulb. When a small animal is seen, draw a ring round it with the finger in the dust and débris, so as not to lose it while a tube or the aspirator is being picked up.

This method allows large quantities of material to be dealt with, and can employ six or more people working as a team at the table.

### iv. *Berlèse funnel* (*fig.* 32)

This was originally designed by the Italian Berlèse for extracting small animals from litter and loose soil. The material is placed in a sieve with not more than four holes to a square inch. This sieve is put inside a large metal funnel which is surrounded by a water jacket heated from underneath.

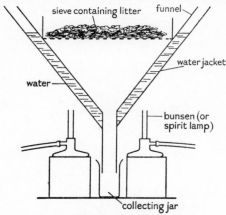

FIG. 32.—Berlèse-type funnel

A jar or killing bottle is put under the funnel. When the water is heated, warm air inside the funnel rises and circulates through the material in the sieve and activates the animals. These fall through the meshes into the receptacle below. Only a very small quantity of material should be put in at a time and it should be left for at least fifteen minutes. Larger quantities need longer treatment.

### v. *Tüllgren funnel* (*fig.* 33)

This is a modified Berlèse funnel in which the source of heat is supplied by a 100-watt electric light bulb suspended from a lid over the funnel. In a small apparatus a 60-watt bulb is enough. This also increases the light which helps to drive the animals downwards.

A combination of the water-jacket and electric light bulb usually produces too much heat, and may cause excessive condensation in the funnel.

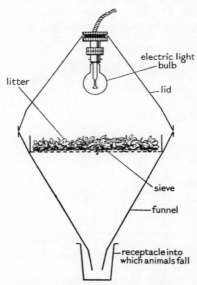

FIG. 33.—A Tüllgren type of funnel

*Note.*—Material for examination with the sieve, Berlèse or Tüllgren funnels, is usually rich in animal life, and is suitable for winter work. Open deciduous woodland on Chalk or other limestone is often well worth trying, especially where beech leaf débris is present (but not as a rule the compacted variety). The bottom part of the litter (the top is usually too dry) is taken, together with the top scraping of soil—5 mm, or about $\frac{1}{6}$ in. Accumulations of leaf rubbish, etc., in small holes and disused rabbit burrows where there is a high relative humidity, are particularly good for examination by methods iii, iv and v, pp. 65–68.

Samples can be collected from different kinds of litter and a comparison of the fauna made. Sacks of material can be kept in store for a week or so before examination, provided it is not allowed to get too dry. For this purpose large quantities are best, as material in small bags dries out too quickly. Each bag or sack should be labelled with a number printed on the outside. It is a good plan to use a cool place for storage.

## vi. *Flotation*

Some animals such as small insects and mites which live in earth or earthy litter can be floated out in water. Special apparatus for this has been designed. Paraffin is stirred into a brine solution and the animals float out into the water-paraffin interface. Excessive foam can be dispersed by a few drops of *iso*-butyl alcohol or tributyl phosphate.

Specimens obtained in this way are usually moribund. Small-scale flotation can be done in tins or pie-dishes.

## vii. *Heat*

Lumps of turf or piles of leaf débris can be heated on hot plates, and the animals caught as they emerge. The temperature must be raised gradually, or the specimens will die inside.

## viii. *Traps and Attrahents*

### (a) *Bait Traps*

Something attractive to the animals, usually food, is put in a container which will allow them to enter but not get out. For small rodents the Longworth Small Mammal Trap* is useful. A small piece of suitable bait, such as biscuit, is put in the inner compartment, with a little paper or cellulose wadding for bedding to prevent the animal dying from exposure. A series of these traps set in the same habitat will give some idea of a rodent or vole population. Traps should be examined first thing

---

* Obtainable from the Longworth Instrument Co., Oxford.

in the morning. For larger animals and birds, trapping is usually not desirable, or even feasible. For ringing birds the Heligoland trap is used at observatories. Ringing nestlings, etc., can also be done by individuals. Details are obtainable from the British Trust for Ornithology, British Museum (Natural History), Cromwell Road, London, S.W.7.

For many ground living invertebrates a simple method is to place the attrahent in a round gold-fish bowl, or jar sunk level with the ground. The top is covered with a piece of tile or glass supported on three stones, this prevents the trap from becoming waterlogged. If the attrahent is a liquid, this is best put in a smaller container inside, and covered with a piece of perforated zinc.

Pieces of swede, carrot, potato, etc., partly buried in the earth attract some animals such as millipedes and woodlice. The pieces are placed in position on the end of a small stick or skewer. These traps should be examined daily.

## (b) *Attrahents*

These are artificial or natural substances which certain animals like. The creatures are caught by the observer. *Sugar* or *treacle* is probably the best-known attrahent. Sugaring mixture is used to catch night-flying insects and some other non-flying invertebrates. It is made of molasses, brown sugar and stale beer boiled together. A few drops of rum, oil of jargonelles or amyl acetate are added before use. The mixture should be kept for as long as possible to mature, and if necessary glucose can be added to stiffen it.

The sugar is painted on to tree trunks or fences just before dusk, preferably on a warm moist night when there is no moon. The best results seem to be obtained from vertical strips, 1 metre (or 3 ft) by 10 cm (4 in.) wide. If the sugar is liable to be absorbed by the surface, an alternative method is to soak a number of pieces of material, such as linen, in the mixture, and hang them in appropriate places by means of a piece of wire previously attached to each. The cloths can be hung in a tin when not in use but they must not be allowed to go mouldy.

There are also other ways of attracting animals. Carcases or meat attracts scavengers, slugs and snails like bran; water attracts some beetles and other insects, especially in dry sandy habitats. It is often instructive to try various attrahents in different places and to experiment with different substances.

Virgin females of some animals, for example the Emperor moth *Saturnia pavonia* (L.), are attractive to the males. Dung attracts some beetles.

### (c) *Chemicals*

Various chemicals acting as repellents can sometimes be used for finding animals. A weak solution of potassium permanganate (see p. 100) poured on to turf will bring earthworms to the surface. Smoke generated from a bee-keeper's smoke gun may dislodge small creatures from cracks in wood and similar places, and water poured into the holes of Dor beetles, *Geotrupes* spp., will bring them to the surface.

The Baermann apparatus, fig. 34, is used for extracting freeliving Nematode worms from soil. Water heated to about 40°C is poured into the funnel so as to half fill it. The material for examination, tied up in a piece of muslin, is suspended above so that it touches the water. The worms are activated by the warm water into which they migrate and in which they are drawn off through the rubber tubing at the bottom of the funnel.

### (d) *Light*

As an attrahent for invertebrates, mainly insects, light can be used in various ways.

1. Light and sheet: this is a sheet suspended with a light behind it, or draped on the ground or over a fence so as to make a reflecting surface. If electricity is available a 150- or 200-watt bulb can be used. This is suspended near the sheet. Observations should be made at frequent intervals. Insects other than moths come to the sheet. "Photoflood" photographer's bulbs (250 or 500 watts) can be used in place of ordinary bulbs; they give a

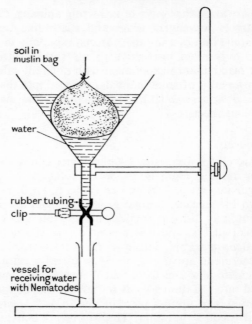

soil in
muslin bag

water

rubber tubing
clip

vessel for
receiving water
with Nematodes

Fig. 34.—Baermann apparatus (section)

brighter light but are more expensive and last for only a few hours. Where electricity is not available a bright paraffin or acetylene lamp is best. Car headlights or small petrol engines for generating a supply of current can be used.

2. Light traps: there are a number of patterns, some of which are complicated in design. They are intended to attract night-flying insects into the trap, from which it is impossible or very difficult for them to get out. Some incorporate a killing agent at the bottom of the trap, but this is not recommended as it results in the needless slaughter of specimens.

The most effective light-trap employs a mercury-vapour lamp. This is a relatively expensive apparatus and electricity is necessary. The trap is usually a round tray made of metal with a rim a few inches high. The lamp is placed in the middle and egg-packing cardboard is placed in the tray. The attraction of the M.V. light to moths and other insects is remarkable, and it is quite usual to find at least four moths in each depression of the cardboard after the light has been used for a few hours.

### ix. *Miscellaneous apparatus for field-work*

(a) *Chisel* for prising off bark from old tree trunks and digging into rotten wood, etc.

(b) *Trowel* for digging into earth, etc., and in dung.

(c) *Aspirator* or *Pooter* (fig. 26). Essential for picking up small invertebrates in large quantities. The tube is best made of perspex or other unbreakable material. If a series of these tubes is available each can be corked and labelled as it is filled or as one moves from one habitat to another. A bottle type of aspirator is shown in fig. 35.

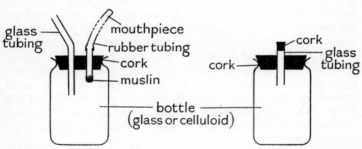

FIG. 35.—Bottle-type aspirator      FIG. 36.—Collecting bottle

(d) *Collecting bottle* (fig. 36). This is useful for small beetles and plant bugs (Hemiptera). The specimens are put in through the small tube which is corked when not in use. The bottle can be used as a killing chamber if an appropriate chemical (see p. 137) is put in it.

(e) *Brush* and *Forceps*. A small, good-quality brush (size 1 or 2), and fine-pointed dissecting forceps are necessary, especially if small invertebrates are put directly in spirit. The wetted top of a piece of grass is a useful substitute for a brush. Two small blunt slithers of wood (such as spills), glued on each side of a piece of cork make a pair of forceps for picking up delicate snail shells, which are liable to be damaged by metal forceps.

(f) *Pie dishes*, preferably enamelled, are useful for sorting weeds and mud from ponds.

(g) A *small sieve* which can be fixed to a long handle is useful for scooping up material from near the edges of ponds, etc.

(h) *Pipettes* with rubber teats are needed for handling small aquatic animals.

(i) *Corked specimen tubes* of assorted sizes are essential for transporting most smaller specimens. Except for pond work they must be kept dry. Penicillin or streptomycin bottles, which can usually be obtained free of charge from the local chemist or doctor, are a useful substitute as they are not easily broken; the rubber tops can be replaced by corks. It is a good plan to make up sets of tubes in flat or other suitable containers.

(j) *Tins, collecting boxes*, etc. These are necessary for transporting larvae, living Lepidoptera, etc.—glass-bottomed collecting tins are preferable to glass-topped ones as most specimens tend to go to the end which is light, and the lid can be put on with the minimum risk of the specimen's escape. Glass-bottomed tins are stronger than similar containers made of cardboard.

(k) *Binoculars* or *field-glasses* are necessary for watching animals at a distance. A pair with magnification about $8 \times 30$ is best. Higher powers are useful for detailed observation but light is reduced and it is difficult to first pick up a moving animal such as a bird in flight. A good *telescope* is usually better for more detailed observation.

(l) An "*Edney*" *paper hygrometer* is an inexpensive and useful instrument for making approximate readings of the Relative

Humidity in grass, holes in trees, etc. Whirling hygrometers are also useful for making a quick determination of the R.H. of the atmosphere. They are available from the usual instrument makers who supply tables to enable the R.H. to be read immediately from the wet- and dry-bulb readings.

(m) *Thermometers*, preferably graduated in the Centigrade scale. Thermometers with reinforced bulbs are obtainable for pushing into soil. A *maximum and minimum thermometer* may be useful for comparison of the outside temperature with that in a hole in the ground or a tree.

(n) *Peterson Grab*, etc. This resembles a small-scale builder's excavator and is used for getting samples of the mud in water in which it is too deep to wade. Other specialised apparatus for taking water samples at known depths, for echo-sounding the depth of mud and so on has been devised, but is unlikely to be needed save for specialised work.

## V. IMPORTANT NOTE

Keep notes of the plant, animal host, locality, preferably with a national grid reference (see p. 140), date and other relevant data of each specimen taken in the field. A piece of paper with this information written in pencil (not indelible), should be placed inside each container or tube. Alternatively each can have a number painted on it in enamel. The numbers are entered in the field note book with the locality, etc., of the specimens. Care must be taken to see that the numbers are not rubbed off: they should not be painted on the corks.

Only a few specimens, those found on the same plant for example, should be put in one container, and those which are known to be, or are suspected as cannibals, like spiders and ground beetles, must be kept separate. It may be desirable to kill some specimens in the field (see p. 136), but no more should be taken than is absolutely necessary for study, and whenever possible these should be brought to the laboratory alive, and released in suitable places after examination.

## VI. RECORDING ANIMALS

A detailed survey of an area requires time, and involves a great deal of work. But even a list of the animals with notes on their occurrence will give much useful information. As Charles Elton has pointed out the number of species of animals (excluding microscopic forms) in any major habitat rarely exceeds 200, and is usually between 60 and 140. Some of the animal ecologist's methods have been described (see p. 59) and it will now be shown how and when these are used.

### i. *Information about the Animal*

When assessing the status of any animal in a community, note as much as possible about its habitat, occurrence and any special feature. A guide to the observations necessary is given below; when possible each observation or capture should receive mention under, (*a*) *name*, (*b*) *numbers*, (*c*) *adult* or *young*, (*d*) *behaviour*, (*e*) *habitat*, (*f*) *time*, (*g*) *weather*.

(*a*) Record the name of the animal, or if this is not known, make as detailed a description of it as possible.

(*b*) How many present? Single, few, etc. Give exact, estimated, or comparative numbers. In the latter case, if the most frequently met species is scored as "5", and the rarest as "1", a rough comparative scale is available. This can be sub-divided if necessary, for example, if an animal appears to be rather more numerous than rare, but not as common as "2", it can be scored as "1·5". This method is more effective if applied independently, that is, between several observers without any collaboration; the results can be compared afterwards, and the average of the findings taken, ignoring any that are very wide of the mean. It must be clearly understood that these numerals are *strictly relative* to the size of the area under survey.

(*c*) Is species adult? Are young present? Record stage of life-cycle where appropriate.

(*d*) Record behaviour under:

1. Feeding: kind of food (full description) and quantity. Classify as follows:

    (α) *Carnivores*, which are sub-divided into—

        *1.* Predators (state prey if known).

        *2.* Parasites (state host if known).

        *3.* Parasitoids (state parasite host if known).

        *4.* Filter feeders on microscopic life (aquatic habitats).

    (β) *Herbivores*, group under—

        *1.* Leaf-feeders—chewing, sucking sap, mining or tunnelling in tissues, etc. (including leaves of non-flowering plants).

        *2.* Bryophyte feeders.

        *3.* Alga and lichen feeders.

        *4.* Filter feeders on microscopic life (aquatic habitats).

        *5.* External fungus feeders, i.e. those which eat fungi but do not actually burrow into them.

        *6.* Internal fungus feeders, i.e. those which feed inside fungi.

        *7.* Bud or shoot feeders.

        *8.* Flower feeders, including pollen eaters.

        *9.* Shoot or stem borers of bushes and herbaceous plants (including non-flowering plants).

        *10.* Wood borers of trees.

        *11.* External fruit and seed feeders.

        *12.* Internal fruit and seed feeders.

        *13.* Those feeding in and under the bark of trees (living or dead)—these may be external fungus feeders.

14. Internal root feeders.
15. External root feeders.
} Any part of a plant below ground level is regarded as "root" for this purpose but the exact morphological part should be stated.

16. Gall formers on aerial parts of plant.
17. Gall formers on subterranean parts of plant.
} State which part or parts of plant.

(γ) *Scavengers*
 1. Those feeding on decaying animal matter, dung, etc.
 2. Those feeding on decaying plant matter.
 3. Those feeding on dead plants and animals.

(δ) *Omnivores*
 Those feeding on both plant and animal material—alive or dead; they may also be part-time scavengers.

2. Movement: by what means? Direction and speed, and possible reason, e.g. avoidance of enemy, to get at food, to get air at surface of pond, etc.

3. Stationary: in what position? On what? Possible reason— hibernation, resemblance to background, feigning death, etc.

4. Mating: note behaviour; one pair or others?

5. Attention to young: food given, how often and how much? Which parent gives it; reactions of young to food and presence of parents, etc.

6. Special features: warning colours? Mimicry? Concealment structure and/or colours? Any other anatomical or physiological "adaptations"?

(*e*) Give a full description of the habitat including vegetation, other animals present, the physiographical features and a map grid reference. The 2½-in. map is best (see p. 140).

(*f*) Give date and time (preferably by the 24-hour clock).

(*g*) Describe weather (see p. 141), temperature, amount of wind (Beaufort scale p. 143), amount of sunshine or light (e.g. eight-eighths cloud if no blue sky can be seen), precipitation, etc. Whenever possible take exact readings.

### (ii) *Preliminary Survey by Listing*

First make a list of the major habitats and work each one systematically dividing the animals into:

(a) *Those observed by day and found by—*

1. Direct observation;
2. The kite net;
3. The sweep net (or water net);
4. The beating tray;
5. Sieving;
6. Flotation of soil;
7. Trapping;
8. Examination of hosts, carcasses or dung, etc. (these may be included under 7 if desirable).

(b) *Those observed at night by—*

1.
2. } As (a) above except that water habitats and beating are
3. } usually effectively and more easily done in daylight;
4.
5.   Trapping by light, sugar, etc.;
6.   As 8 above; different host animals may enter the area at night.

Though most diurnal and nocturnal animals appear in "shifts" some species overlap, and these should be noted, with the time of their appearance.

7

## Section E

# COMPREHENSIVE PLANT AND ANIMAL SURVEYS

When practice has been gained in recording plants and animals, a survey of an area such as a wood or a common can be made, to show as much as possible of the wild life and its relationships to the surroundings—rock, soil, climate, etc., as well as the influence of the plants and animals, including man, on one another. This is an ecological survey, for which a team of workers is usually needed, though one or two people can do good work in a small area. The time that can be given to the survey must be considered, and this and the number of workers, together with their experience and the available facilities, will determine the size of the area.

First make a list of the major habitats of the area, and if possible mark them on a 6-in. map. It is not always easy to define precisely the limits of each habitat, but the help of a geological map, if the area covers more than one formation, and a careful consideration of the vegetation and soils, usually give a fairly good working basis, the details of which can later be modified as the area becomes better known.

Though it is best to divide the area into its natural regions or habitats, it may be more convenient to have artificial divisions. For example, an area of heathland may be intersected by paths or roads, which divide it into a number of *loculi* (singular *loculus*).

The layers of vegetation, topographical features including differences in altitude and aspect, as well as any features like a pond, stream or swamp, must be recorded. Fresh water habitats should be listed and classified separately from the land habitats.

Agricultural land and built up areas must be taken into account. Each major habitat should be worked systematically.

(*I*) Begin by making a soil map and a number of monoliths illustrating the profiles at selected sites, to show soil changes from one habitat to another (see p. 28).

(*II*) List the plants and animals of each habitat, arranging them in their correct taxonomic order according to modern catalogues (see p. 124). Notes of their frequency of occurrence, preferably in annotated form, such as "*d, a, f, o, r*" for plants (see p. 42), and the 1–5 scale for animals (see p. 76), should be recorded.

(*III*) If the survey can be continued so that seasonal changes are shown, listing must be repeated at intervals. Make sure the day and night aspects of animal life are adequately studied.

(*IV*) Make a map to show the plant communities and associations. It is not necessary to do this in great detail, though obviously the more information which can be included the better. Selected areas of quadrats or transects typical of the different communities can be studied in detail later. Fig. 37 shows a vegetation map of plant communities.

(*V*) Map the distribution of the more important animals which are the major biotic factors in the area (see p. 40). These will be the larger species or the bigger communities of smaller animals, e.g. badger or rabbit colonies, or areas where birds come to feed regularly.

(*VI*) When a general survey has been done detailed attention can be given to the more interesting habitats, or to specific problems within the area. In a survey of this kind it is usually profitable to compare and contrast the species of the different habitats, and to try and find out how they are "adapted" to these habitats. It is helpful to remember the importance of soil types, the kind and layering of the vegetation, and that the three important things in the lives of animals are food, shelter and a mate.

(*VII*) When detailed problems, or the survey of a limited habitat are considered, it may be found desirable to continue

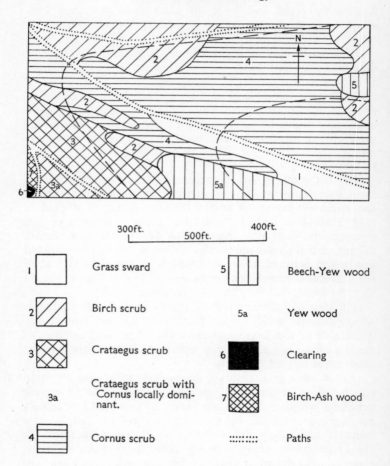

|   |   |   |   |
|---|---|---|---|
| 1 | Grass sward | 5 | Beech-Yew wood |
| 2 | Birch scrub | 5a | Yew wood |
| 3 | Crataegus scrub | 6 | Clearing |
| 3a | Crataegus scrub with Cornus locally dominant. | 7 | Birch-Ash wood |
| 4 | Cornus scrub | :::::::: | Paths |

FIG. 37.—Plant communities on a Chalk spur near Juniper Hall Field Centre, Box Hill, Surrey, 1948

*(Modified from a map made by the Botany Department, University of Manchester.)*

## NOTES ON FIG. 37

1. Grass sward with seedlings of *Betula verrucosa* and *Cornus sanguinea*. Grasses and all other plants stunted. *Poterium sanguisorba*—(l d) (see p. 42), *Euphrasia* sp.—(a), *Anagalis arvensis*, *Echium vulgare*, *Teucrium scorodonia* (increasing up the slope).

2. Birch scrub. Oldest birch along lower slope, younger and more scattered trees up the slope gradually merging into *Cornus sanguinea* scrub in 4.

3. *Crataegus monogyna* scrub with some old and young *Betula verrucosa*. Eight species of grass (listed)—the following are locally dominant— *Festuca ovina*, *Brachypodium sylvaticum*, and *Bromus erectus*. Fourteen spp. herbaceous present all of robust growth. The following shrubs were noted:—*Cornus sanguinea* (a), *Ligustrum vulgare* (o), *Fagus sylvatica*— young, *Sorbus aria*, *Viburnum lantana*, *Rosa canina*, *Rosa* sp., *Prunus spinosa*, *Rhamnus catharticus*, *Juniperus communis* (vr).

3a. *Crataegus monogyna* scrub with *Cornus sanguinea* locally dominant.

4. *Cornus sanguinea* scrub of varying density merging into 2 below and apparently extending up the slope into 1. Above the 400-ft contour the soil is poor in humus, very strong with angular flints and few herbaceous plants; mosses and lichens are abundant.

5. Beech-Yew wood on steep slope. *Mercurialis perennis* locally dominant under and between trees.

5a. Yew wood with a few *Sorbus aria*. Some *Nepeta hederacea* and yew seedlings present. *Teucrium scorodonia* and *Mercurialis perennis* near edges of wood.

6. Clearing—no vegetation.

7. Birch-Ash wood at an early stage.

---

observations over a number of years, and to extend investigations outside the area. A general background of the ecology of the region will be found invaluable, and the preliminary survey should be done first by each worker in close contact with his colleagues. For instance, no ornithologist should be without at least a working knowledge of insects, or he should have reasonable access to such knowledge. A knowledge of plants is also useful as many birds are insectivorous (and many insects are found only on specific plants), or they feed on seeds or fruits. The entomologist should be able to identify at least the commoner birds, some of which may be controlling factors in insect populations. The wider one's knowledge the better one's position to specialise later on any particular problem.

(*VIII*) In a long-term survey certain data such as weather records (see p. 141), artificial disturbance of vegetation, or diversion of waterways, may prove useful, or even necessary, to account for some observations made during several seasons. It is worth keeping such records, even if their immediate use may not always be apparent.

(*IX*) In all survey records it is important to know the source of identification of specimens and of the field data. Observers must place their initials or name after each record or observation. It is convenient to keep a card index of all records. Specimens of critical groups should be kept for reference or checking where necessary by specialists.

(*X*) Make distribution maps of the more important species of plants and animals. These can be superimposed on the geological, topographical or other maps, if they are made on transparent paper and to the same scale.

Section F

# THE SEA-SHORE AND ESTUARY

## I. INTRODUCTION

Our coastal shores of rock, sand, shingle and mud, as well as river estuaries, have for long been an outdoor laboratory for biologists. Not only is there great variety in the species of plants and animals inhabiting these places, but many show interesting anatomical and physiological "adaptations" to their environment and way of life.

The sea-shore is difficult to define precisely, but it may be taken to cover the area between the lowest and highest spring tides. This intertidal zone is uncovered twice each day by the ebb-tide, and the plants and animals are temporarily exposed to much the same climatic conditions as exist in some land habitats. Seasonal variation is not so marked as on land.

The chief types of habitat found on sea-shores may be summarised:

(i) *Rocky shores*

    (a) rocks—surfaces and crevices,
    (b) rock pools.

(ii) *Sandy shores*

    (a) the moist sand,
    (b) pools left by ebbing tide.

(iii) *Muddy shores*

    (a) the moist mud,
    (b) pools left by ebbing tide.

(iv) *Shingle beaches*

(v) *Estuaries*—the type of substratum—e.g. mud, gravel, sand, shingle, etc.

(vi) *Man-made structures* such as breakwaters, pier-piles, etc.

There is, of course, infinite detailed variety of habitat on any type of shore, as well as in estuaries. A shingle beach, for example, may grade into a rocky shore towards low-tide mark, or localised areas of mud may occur between sandy patches, both of which may contain smaller or larger pools left by the receding tide.

The plants and animals of most intertidal zones of shore or estuary are characteristically distributed in a well-defined pattern, and the factors determining their distribution fall under the headings of:

(*a*) The nature of the substratum.

(*b*) Temperature range of the water, and the air temperature during periods of exposure.

(*c*) Light—especially on a rocky shore.

(*d*) The drying effects of wind and sun during exposure (the latter does not apply when low tide occurs during darkness).

(*e*) Wave action—the physical pounding by waves and the influence of spray caused by them.

(*f*) The chemistry of the water—especially the pH, and, most important in estuaries and places where rivers flow into the sea, is the dilution effect of incoming fresh water, which often varies from time to time in the same place.

(*g*) The biotic relationships of the plants and animals themselves, as well as the influence of man, chiefly through the removal of species for commercial purposes, as for example, crabs, lobsters, and seaweed for manure.

## II. METHODS OF STUDY

*To observe the lowest zones on any shore it is necessary to carry out the work during the three days after a new or full moon.*

## i. *The Rocky Shore*

Make a profile transect (see p. 44) from the zone above high-tide level, to as far as possible down the beach. It is important to plot the profile accurately (see p. 45). Where the vegetation varies greatly at the same level, a belt transect (see p. 47), which will not show the profile, can be made in addition and will show changes in the vegetation. At the appropriate places on the profile, or at the side of the belt transect, list the animals present. If possible, make an estimate of the numbers of the latter, e.g. "abundant", "common", "few", "very few". Fig. 38 shows the relationship between vegetation and fauna on a sea-shore. For a more detailed population count of the plants and animals, make a distribution curve of the numbers of each species which can be counted separately using any convenient but sufficiently large sample areas (see p. 47) taken at regular intervals along the transect. Plot the number of each species per unit area against the sea-level, alternatively set out the results in table form (fig. 39).

Small rock pools are best mapped separately; they usually show a zoning of the vegetation, since the bottom regions correspond with the deeper zones of the sea-shore. A contour map of a pool can be made by stretching a marked or knotted string (for example in decimetre intervals), over the pool from place to place, and measuring the depth with a marked stick. It is convenient to do this direct to scale on squared paper. Stationary animals like anemones and limpets can be mapped. Others—the free-swimming species must be listed.

Make notes on the ecology and any "adaptations" of the plants and animals observed, e.g.

(*a*) How are the plants attached to the substratum?

(*b*) How do the animals attach themselves to the rock? If they do not, do they find shelter in any other way, such as in the seaweeds?

(*c*) Do any plants and animals possess special structures for moisture retention, or do they only occur in rock pools

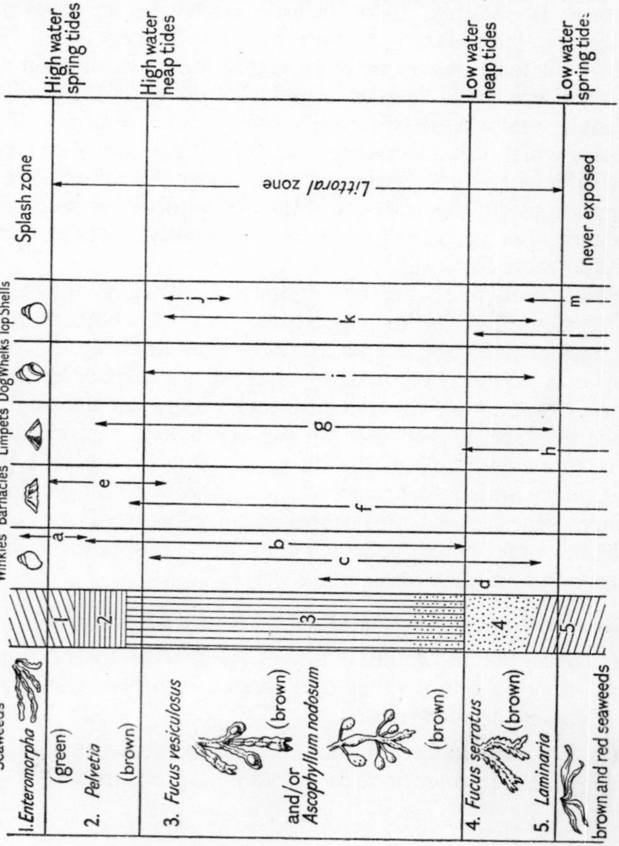

FIG. 38.—The chief seaweed zones and animal distribution on a rocky sea-shore, Isle of Man. *The information in this table was kindly supplied by Miss Hazel M. Meredith of the Zoology Department, Reading University.*

Key to the animals.

a = *Litorina neritoides* (L.)
b = *L. saxatalis* (Olivi) (= *rudis* Maton)
c = *L. litoralis* (L.)
d = *L. litorea* (L.)
e = *Chthamalus stellatus* Ranz.
f = *Balanus* spp.
g = *Patella vulgata* L.
h = *P. athletica* Bean
i = *Nucella lapillus* (L.)
j = *Monodonta lineata* (da Costa)
k = *Gibbula umbilicalis* (da Costa)
l = *G. cineraria* (L.)
m = *Calliostoma zizyphinum* (L.)

High water spring tides
High water neap tides
Low water neap tides
Low water spring tides

Splash zone
*Littoral* zone
never exposed

Winkles   Barnacles   Limpets   DogWhelks   Top Shells

Seaweeds
1. *Enteromorpha* (green)
2. *Pelvetia* (brown)
3. *Fucus vesiculosus* (brown) and/or *Ascophyllum nodosum* (brown)
4. *Fucus serratus* (brown)
5. *Laminaria*
brown and red seaweeds

*The distribution and relative abundance of some animals on a rocky shore near Port Erin, Isle of Man*

Sample areas (each 1 sq. yd.)

| | 1 | 2 | 3 | 4 | 5 | 6 | 7 | 8 | 9 | 10 | 11 | 12 | 13 | 14 | 15 | 16 | 17 | 18 | 19 | 20 | 21 | 22 | 23 | 24 | 25 | 26 | 27 | 28 | 29 | 30 |
|---|---|---|---|---|---|---|---|---|---|---|---|---|---|---|---|---|---|---|---|---|---|---|---|---|---|---|---|---|---|---|
| Litorina saxatilis (Olivi) | – | 3 | – | 5 | 3 | 1 | 7 | 2 | 2 | 11 | 4 | 1 | 3 | 2 | 2 | – | – | – | – | – | – | 1 | – | – | – | – | – | – | – | – |
| L. litoralis (L.) | 3 | 5 | 1 | – | – | – | 1 | – | – | 5 | – | 1 | 5 | 6 | 6 | 10 | 6 | 12 | 10 | 5 | 10 | 8 | 15 | 10 | 4 | 4 | 3 | 5 | 5 | 2 |
| L. litorea (L.) | – | 2 | – | – | – | – | 1 | – | 2 | 3 | 1 | – | – | 3 | 2 | 4 | 12 | 8 | 3 | 16 | – | – | 4 | 4 | – | – | – | – | – | – |
| Gibbula umbilicalis (da Costa) | – | – | – | – | – | – | – | – | 1 | 1 | – | – | – | – | – | 1 | – | 1 | – | – | 1 | 1 | – | 3 | 1 | 1 | – | – | 2 | 3 |
| G. cineraria (L.) | – | – | – | – | – | – | – | – | 1 | – | 1 | – | – | – | – | 1 | 1 | 1 | 2 | – | – | 5 | 3 | 3 | 3 | – | – | – | – | – |
| Actinia equina L. | – | – | – | – | – | – | – | – | – | 1 | – | – | 1 | – | – | 1 | – | 1 | – | – | – | – | – | – | – | – | – | – | – | – |
| Nucella lapillus (L.) | – | – | – | – | – | – | – | – | – | – | – | 2 | 1 | 1 | – | 2 | 3 | – | 1 | 2 | – | – | – | 1 | 4 | 2 | 4 | 5 | – | – |
| Patella vulgata L. | – | – | – | – | – | – | – | – | – | – | – | 1 | 3 | 2 | 5 | 4 | 2 | 6 | 2 | 4 | 1 | – | 1 | 2 | 8 | 1 | 4 | 1 | 2 | – |
| Balanus sp. | a | a | a | 50 | 25 | – | – | – | – | – | – | – | – | – | – | – | – | – | – | – | – | – | – | – | – | – | – | – | – | a |
| Porifera | – | – | – | – | – | – | – | – | – | – | – | – | – | – | – | – | – | – | – | – | – | 1 | o | o | o | o | f | f | a | a |

a = abundant
f = frequent
o = occasional

| Pelvetia canaliculata (L.) |
| Fucus spiralis L. |
| Ascophyllum nodosum Le Jol. |

Fucus serratus L.

Laminaria sp.
Fucus vesiculosus L.

High water spring tide     High (Neap)     Low (Neap)     Low water spring tide

Fig. 39.—The information in this table was kindly supplied by Miss Hazel M. Meredith of the Zoology Department, Reading University.

or well down below the high-tide mark, where they are only uncovered for relatively short periods?

(*d*) Do any of the organisms live mostly or entirely on the shady side of rocks?

(*e*) Do any of the animals show colour "adaptations"?

(*f*) Do any animals show special feeding "adaptations"?

## ii. *The Sandy Shore*

This is not so rich in plant and animal life, and the latter is usually found in, rather than on, the sand, and the species feed mainly on organic material and plankton. Most of the animals live in a burrow or tube in the sand, and this has the advantage of protecting the creatures from adverse effects of temperature changes and enemies, and enables them to live in a relatively stable medium below the surface of the sand, where with increasing depth the salinity is less altered by changes in the salt content of the water above.

Zonation of the fauna can only be appreciated by digging out the animals. The best method of studying a sandy beach is to pass a series of samples (taken to the same depth) through a fine mesh sieve, such as a flour sifter. The samples should be taken fairly close together in groups, and each group must be separated by regular intervals between high- and low-tide marks (a large number of small samples is preferable to a few large ones). In this way the relative numbers of species can also be found.

Note that the "adaptations" of these animals concern chiefly the methods of burrowing and of getting food. Where possible it is helpful to keep these animals in an aquarium where closer observations can be made on their habits (see p. 93).

## iii. *The Muddy Shore*

Stretches of mud occur typically in estuaries (see (v), p. 91). Small patches of mud, sometimes due to exposed clay on the shoreline, occur in places, but are frequently graded into sand or intermixed with rocks. An interesting contrast in the species and in numbers of plants and animals can be seen on such shores, which are well suited to study by both the transect and quadrat methods (see pp. 44, 47). Pools in mud may harbour some of the smaller free-swimming animals left behind by the receding tide.

### iv. *Shingle Beaches*

Shingle usually occurs in patches mixed with rocks, or it may grade into sand. Owing to the liability of the individual pebbles to be moved, and the relatively large space between them, which allows of very little deposition of organic material, shingle is biologically an almost barren substratum.

### v. *Estuaries*

The water of a swiftly flowing river is fresh to its mouth, and the estuary as here considered falls within the study of a fresh-water habitat. In flat estuaries and creeks where the rise and fall of the tide over a long distance causes varying salinity in the water, physical conditions are often very complicated, and all stages between slightly brackish water and sea water may exist. In such places extensive deposits of mud and sand often occur.

Other environmental factors are also important. In shallow water the desiccating effect of winds and sun during ebb tide, may restrict the range of some plants and animals, and the temperature of sandy or muddy flats covered only by a shallow layer of water may rise to a point beyond the tolerance of many species.

Light penetration may be reduced by the amount of sediment brought down by a river, and this results in a direct reduction of the plant life, and indirectly of the fauna. Such effects are well seen in estuaries where the river enters at a slow rate, and the rise and fall of the tide is gentle.

The study of an estuary may present certain problems, not the least of which may be the physical difficulty of reaching some of the more inaccessible, and sometimes dangerous, parts of mud and sand flats. A generalised sketch map of the estuary should first be made to show the distribution of the chief types of plants and animals. Study distinct areas separately, for example, mud and sand patches.

Where the substratum consists largely of mud, the fine particles impose special conditions upon the plants and animals. Though ideal for anchorage for the long-rooted Eel Grass *Zostera nana* Roth. it offers little anchorage and opportunity for colonisation by many seaweeds. Animals likewise find it difficult to attach themselves to this substratum, and most of the species are burrowers or tube dwellers whose feeding and respiration mechanisms are specially "adapted" to this environment.

The upper zones of plants and animals can be recorded by transect—preferably belt transect (see p. 47) as the species may be scattered, or they can be recorded by a number of carefully chosen sample areas of, for example, 1 square metre each. In the lower regions, the vegetation is mapped and the animals listed and counted in typical sample areas. Each sample area should be taken to a uniform depth (say $\frac{1}{2}$ metre or less according to the species of animals present), and each must be carefully sieved through a fine mesh. A topographical profile should be recorded beside the belt transect (see p. 44). Zonation of plants and animals is often well seen along the sides of an estuary, and is influenced largely by the degree of salinity.

## vi. *Man-made Structures*

In many respects such substrata as breakwaters, pier groynes, concrete piers, etc., function as pieces of rock, and the colonisers of the rocky shore are often found on them, even when the structures are isolated amid extensive mud or sand areas. Burrowing (in wood and stone) and encrusting forms comprise the typical fauna of this habitat, and certain seaweeds become attached to the different substrata. The plants and animals often show a well-marked vertical distribution, which can sometimes effectively be recorded photographically. A narrow vertical belt transect will usually show this zonation, and counts per unit area of the animals along the transect, or at the side in the same zones, will give a record of the relative numbers of each species. It is important to ascertain the height of each zone relative to the base of the structure. Note also if there is any difference in the distribution of the plants and animals on the different sides of the structure, for example, does any species prefer the sheltered side away from the prevailing direction of the waves?

### III. SOME GENERAL CONSIDERATIONS OF THE SEA-SHORE

The plants and many of the animals are fixed to the substratum on which they occur. Some, like limpets and winkles, move within a limited area. The migrations of the latter offer good opportunities for observation, by marking them with a spot of "Joy Brushing Enamel" and tracing their wanderings.

Denuded quadrats on hard substrata can be kept under observation, and the colonisation by plants and animals investigated (see p. 44), the quadrat can be marked with paint, or marks can be made in the rock. Colonisation by the plants and animals is nearly always effected in their young stages. The animals are often free-swimming and living more in the open sea. The nauplius larvae of certain Crustacea, and the free-living larvae of limpets, are well-known examples, an account of which, together with the life-cycles of other species, will be found in any good book on marine biology (see p. 155).

As indicated, the most interesting "adaptations" of life around the shores, are those concerned with the problems of water conservation, feeding, breathing and maintaining a position in or on the substratum. It is here that a marine aquarium can be a most useful adjunct to the work done on the shore. The setting up of a marine aquarium is not quite as simple as that of a fresh-water tank, and those who live by, or near the sea, will find it an easier undertaking. For others the little extra trouble will be more than repaid by the excellent opportunities a marine tank offers for observation. A useful account of the installation and upkeep of marine aquaria will be found in the *Science Masters' Book*, part III, "Biology", pp. 52 and 144. All-glass containers are best, as metal rapidly corrodes in contact with sea water.

The study of a shore should always be carried out with consideration to the rocks exposed both on the shore itself, and in the immediate zone above the high-tide level. The influence of man as a biotic factor must also be taken into account, and it is often instructive to extend the study of the upper zones of a shore into maritime habitats, such as sand-dunes and salt-marshes, where the methods already described for land-habitats are applicable.

Instructive comparative studies can be made of the life and conditions on different kinds of shores, as well as on the same kinds of shore in different parts of the country.

For a bibliography, see p. 155.

## Section G

# PROJECTS

### Introduction

The possibilities for field work in a district will soon be seen by the enthusiastic and enterprising, and it is hoped that the methods given in the preceding pages will be helpful.

The present section deals with a number of field projects which can be undertaken either as long-term or short-term studies. Much depends on the available time and means. Many projects could be suggested, and these given here should be regarded only as selected examples to show the possible range and type of such work.

When choosing a piece of ground for a survey, four points should be considered:

(*i*) that the terrain is suitable for the type of work in mind,

(*ii*) that in a long-term survey it will not be built over, or drastically modified in any way before the work is completed,

(*iii*) that it will not be subjected to too much disturbance by the presence of humans, cattle, etc.,

(*iv*) that it is accessible to the surveyors. If a piece of private ground is chosen, permission to work there MUST first be obtained and the requests of the owners must be scrupulously observed; no damage must be done, gates should be closed. Inform the owners of any wish to mark out areas with pegs and of any kinds of traps used.

I. Observations on the Badger *Meles meles meles* (L.)

The European Badger is a carnivore which, with the Otter *Lutra lutra* (L.), Pine Marten *Martes martes* (L.), Stoat *Mustela erminea stabilis* B.H., Weasel *M. nivalis nivalis* L. and Polecat *M. putorius* L., belongs to the family Mustelidae. The badger has a wide range in Europe and Asia, and occurs all over the British Isles, except in the Isle of Man and some other islands. It is essentially a woodland species, and is scarce in flat sparsely wooded parts of the country like East Anglia. Owing to its nocturnal habits it is often overlooked, and it is commoner in many districts than is realised. Colonies sometimes occur quite near human habitations.

Observations can be made (*A*) to determine the presence of badgers and (*B*) on the living animals.

(*A*) Farmers, gamekeepers, museum staff may be able to give some useful information. Look for the following signs:

1. Tracks which are much wider than rabbits, and on which there are no pellets. These tracks go *under* fences, on which the characteristic black and white hairs may be caught on the wire, or on a rough piece of wooden paling. When the earth is moist the five-toed pad marks should be looked for; the forefeet are wider than the hind ones. Try to follow the tracks back to the burrows or setts.

2. Numerous "snuffle holes" made by the nose, where the badgers have searched for worms and other soil invertebrates. These holes are usually narrower than the scrapes dug by rabbits, and there are no pellets near them. Occasionally a hole is used as a dung-pit.

3. Dung-pits. These are small holes often made near the setts and used for regular deposition of dung. The state of this —fresh or old—gives some indication of when the badger was last in the locality.

4. "Tip heaps" or large piles of earth and rock which indicate the tremendous excavations made by these animals. In Chalk country the heaps may be visible at a distance in a wooded copse or a hillside.

5. Claw-marks on trees; pad marks in mud, and in well-trodden "play-grounds".

6. Bedding—grass, bracken, leaves, moss, etc., near to, or in the entrances of the setts, especially in spring and autumn.

7. Elder, *Sambucus nigra* L., Burdock *Arctium* spp. and Nettle *Urtica dioica* L., often grow by the colonies. These plants are not touched by the badgers.

8. Hairs may be present outside the entrance to the setts.

9. Setts which are used regularly are free from plant débris and spiders webs, and the earth outside is well-trodden, unless the sett was recently made or reopened. Flies may be present at the entrance.

10. Small ventilation holes are made from the tunnels, usually not far from the mouth of the sett. The badger makes them with its nose from within, and they are usually two or three inches wide.

11. The presence of a fox can usually be determined by its strong smell and by bones, feathers, fur, etc., round the entrance to the hole.

12. Place one or two twigs vertically across the entrance to the sett. If on later examination these have been removed or brushed aside, a badger may have passed in or out.

(*B*) Badgers come out of their setts at dusk. Watch their behaviour near the entrances, especially when the young begin to come above ground, usually during April.

1. Do not wear light-coloured clothing or rainproofs liable to crackle. Warm clothing is essential as the temperature drops after dusk.

2. Take a good torch; one with an adjustable beam is best, and it must on no account make any noise as it is switched on.

3. Go to the colony well before dusk. If possible choose a background against which to sit, or climb a tree. It is best to be not nearer than six or seven yards from a sett which shows signs of regular use.

4. If the colony is near a much used footpath, the badgers do not usually take much notice of human scent. But it is always best to take up a position downwind.

5. Absolute silence is necessary all the time.

6. Remember that noises are magnified at night. A beetle rustling in the leaves may sound like a badger to the inexperienced watcher. The first indication of a badger's presence may be the sound of the animal scratching itself.

7. Ground bait—biscuits, cake, honey, etc., may attract a badger into a place where it can easily be seen.

Make the following observations:

(*i*) The badger has short limbs and is a good shape for moving in a tunnel. Compare with the fox which is mainly a surface-living animal.

(*ii*) The black and white striped face. This is warning coloration (see p. 103). The black stripes tend to conceal the eyes.

(*iii*) The coat is lighter in colour on the back. This is an example of inverted counter-shading (see p. 103).

(*iv*) If possible note that the legs are well adapted for digging, and that the forefeet are broader than the hind ones.

(*v*) Note the animal's habits. It is usually very cautious when coming out of the sett. It has a good sense of smell and hearing, but its sight is poor. The badger scratches frequently —due more often to a dry skin than to parasites.

(*vi*) What noise does it make? Distinguish the puppy-like yelps of young and adults when playing, the gutteral purring request voice and "scream" which is more often made when the badger is away from the sett.

(*vii*) If a series of observations can be made note the times of emergence from the sett. Plot these on a graph against the time of sunset for the different seasons.

(*viii*) Analyse the dung and make notes on its composition so far as the remains can be identified. It may be necessary to tease some out in water. Microscopical examination should be made for earthworm setae.

REFERENCE

NEAL, E. *The Badger*, Collins, London, 1948.

## II. TESTING COLOUR PERCEPTION IN THE HONEY-BEE
### *APIS MELLIFERA* (L.)

*Apparatus needed:* (1) white topped table; (2) honey slightly diluted with water; (3) twigs; (4) painted pieces of glass—old $3\frac{1}{4} \times 3\frac{1}{4}$-in. lantern slides are suitable; paint four slides of each of the following colours:—black, white, green, red, blue, mauve and two or three different shades of grey; (5) yellow "Joy Brushing Enamel"; (6) a small paint brush (size 0 or 1). Note: the painted glasses must be used unpainted side uppermost.

*Method:* 1. Put the table in a sunny place, preferably not within about nine yards (or eight metres) of a bee hive. Put a little honey on a blue glass and place it on the table and leave it. Start this experiment fairly early in the day. The jar of honey must be kept well away from the table.

2. If no bees come to the table within half an hour or so, dip a small twig in the honey (do not use a metal or glass rod to do this), and try to induce a bee feeding or gathering pollen at the nearest flower to take some. While it is thus engaged, walk slowly to the table and gently manoeuvre the bee so as to leave it feeding from the plate. Watch the bee carefully and note what it does after feeding. If you wish to see if the first bee comes back again, put a tiny dab of "Joy Brushing Enamel" on the thorax; the specimen can then be recognised again. After a while more bees should come to the honey. Note the number.

3. Remove the blue glass with the honey to indoors and wash it. Put out a clean blue, and a clean red glass, side by side, both without honey. Note the number of bees coming to each glass.

If most bees go to the blue glass then they are able to distinguish between blue and red, but this does not prove that they distinguish them as colours, or by shade difference, as in a black and white photograph.

4. Place on the table a blue glass with honey, and surround it with glasses of different shades varying from white through

greys to black. Frequently change the position of *all* the glasses so as to eliminate any possible bias due to the bee's memory. When the bees have congregated on the blue glass for a time, remove all the glasses and replace them by a new set of one blue, and similar pieces of white, grey and glack glass, all without honey. These need not be exactly the same as previously. Note the results. If the bees now congregate on the blue glass this proves they have a true colour perception sense. The possibility that the bees have used smell to distinguish the colours could be eliminated by using different brands of paints on the glasses. In his original experiments, von Frisch used coloured cards, and to eliminate smell he covered these with ordinary glass.

5. If bees are trained to come to a red plate, and then a clean red, and a clean black plate, are put side by side, the bees will be found to go to each in about equal numbers. They cannot distinguish between red and black.

6. If various other coloured glasses, but no white, grey or black ones are used, it will be found that the bees confuse various colours. Try this and note which ones. It can be shown that bees' appreciation of colour is poor at the red end of the spectrum. But they can distinguish colours well into the ultra-violet up to a wavelength of 300 millimicrons.

7. These findings are worth considering in relation to the flowers which the honey-bee visits. Make a list of plants in flower in the locality, and note the colours of each, and if they are visted by honey-bees.

REFERENCES

BUTLER, C. *The World of the Honeybee*, Collins, London, 1954.
VON FRISCH, K. *Bees, their Vision, Chemical Senses, and Language*, Cornell University Press, Ithaca, N.Y., 1950.

III. STUDIES OF EARTHWORM POPULATIONS

Earthworms will come to the surface if a dilute solution of potassium permanganate is poured on to the soil and allowed to soak in. Not all the earthworms are extracted, and it does not follow that a consistent proportion can be counted from all samples, so that the true relative abundance of earthworms in different soils cannot be studied. But the method is useful for gaining a rough idea of the populations from contrasted soil-types, and also the presence or absence of species.

*Method:* choose a number of sites on different soils, preferably in easily accessible places as the solution has to be taken to the sites, or alternatively, if water is available, solutions can be made up locally.

For each sample mark out one square metre. Remove all superficial vegetation but do not disturb the roots. Treat each square metre with 6·8 litres (1½ gallons) of solution made up at the rate of 1·5 grams ($\frac{1}{19}$ oz) of crystals per litre. Examine each treated area after the solution has had time to soak in. This usually takes some minutes. When no more worms come to the surface conclude the count for the sample.

Take a number of samples, say four, each about half a one-pound jam jar full from the soil adjacent to each sample area. Mix these well and make the mass of soil into a cone. Divide this into four and analyse a sample from one quarter for its humus content and test its pH (see p. 116).

To determine the humus content of soil first weigh it. Burn it thoroughly in a suitable container, then weigh it again. The loss of weight represents the amount of humus burnt and the water driven off. For practical purposes, and unless the soil is waterlogged, the water content can be ignored; or if preferred, the soil can be air dried before weighing and burning.

Is there any correlation between humus content (and type of humus), pH and the species of earthworms of different soils?

### IV. STUDIES OF ANIMAL TRACKS

Records of tracks can be kept in three ways:

1. By drawing or diagrams
2. By photographs
3. By plaster-casts

Good diagrams or drawing are always worth making. Photography is an undertaking for those with experience, as close-up pictures will be needed. There are a number of books on photography which adequately cover this subject (see p. 156). Plaster-casts are the most realistic way of recording animal tracks.

*Materials needed:* 1. Dental plaster of Paris; 2. A mixing bowl and spoon; 3. Strips of smooth shiny plastic material; the width and length will vary according to the size of the print, but 2 in. by about 2 ft, would be the maximum needed (for deer's "slots"); 4. Wire paper clips; 5. Newspaper.

*Method:* choose a good print. Surround it with a strip of plastic clipped together at its ends, so as to enclose the print in the middle of a minimum area. Mix the plaster with water so that it runs like fairly thick cream and pour this into the print. It will take at least ten minutes to set hard. Then remove it carefully, the plastic will come away without sticking, and can be used any number of times. Wrap the cast carefully in newspaper without removing any soil which sticks to it. Carefully wash off all earth and mud in the laboratory. Smear the cast lightly with vaseline, and press it gently into a semi-liquid bed of plaster of Paris, prepared in a plastic surround or an old box, and allow it to harden. The original cast or negative is then removed, and can be used for making any number of positives.

### REFERENCE

SPEAKMAN, F. J. *Tracks, Trials and Signs*, G. Bell & Sons Ltd., London, 1954.

## V. A STUDY IN ADAPTIVE COLORATION

Some insects, and other animals, by their colour, form and apparent surface texture, show a close resemblance to parts of plants, such as buds, leaves and twigs. Some Hemiptera (plant bugs), Coleoptera (Beetles), larvae of Lepidoptera (Butterflies and Moths) fall in this group, and some are probably specific to certain plants. These species show *mimicry*.

Other animals seem to get adequate protection from their cryptic devices without resembling any specific structure of a plant. Their shape and colour patterns conform to various parts of the general background, such as light and shade, cracks, holes, leaf-curls, etc. These are examples of *cryptic coloration*.

In both the above there is usually an underlying elimination of (1) roundness of form (by counter-shading), (2) outline (by chequered borders, coincident patterns, etc.) and (3) shadows (by assuming suitable positions, orientation to the sun, etc.).

By contrast *aposematic* or *warning colours* are always bright —usually red, black, white and yellow or any combination of these. The wearers of these colours have some powerful method of offence or defence, unless they happen to be animals themselves harmless and mimicing ones which are not, in which case they are *mimics*.

Make notes and sketches of the exact position and circumstances in which animals of these three categories are found. Choose a well defined habitat such as a piece of waste ground, meadow or a wood. Extend the survey if possible so as to cover all the spring and summer months. A collection of specimens should be made to illustrate the survey.

### REFERENCES

COTT, H. B. *Adaptive Coloration in Animals*, Methuen & Co. Ltd., London, 1940.

STEPHENSON, E. M., & CHARLES, S. *Animal Camouflage*, A. & C. Black Ltd., London, 1955.

## VI. COLONISATION

1. By plants on land (denuded quadrat, see p. 47). Remove the vegetation from a square metre of turf leaving as much earth as possible. It is permissible to dig the patch so as to get out the roots. At regular intervals, for example, once every three months, map the plants growing in the square.

2. By animals on the bottom of a pebbly stream. Make a frame of wood about $\frac{1}{3}$ square metre and cover it with fine

metal gauze strengthened underneath with wire-netting. Cover the tray with a layer of pebbles or gravel, making it as similar to the bottom of the stream as possible. Leave it on the bed of the stream for a few weeks. It can then be lifted out, and the sample will show which animals have colonised the area of the frame, and will give some idea of their numbers.

3. Areas on a rock, breakwater, etc., on the sea-shore can be denuded of plants and animals and recolonisation can be watched.

## VII. Effect of Trampling on Herbaceous Vegetation

Choose an area of sward such as a meadow or piece of common land with a path (on no account enter a private field which is to be hayed even if there is a right of way through). Make a number of detailed line transects across the path starting well into the untrodden vegetation on one side, and ending similarly on the opposite side of the path (see p. 49).

A series of ten quadrats ($\frac{1}{4}$ square metre for example) taken (1) on the path and (2) in the sward, on one or each side of the path, is a useful supplement to this record. Record species as "present" or "absent" and work out their percentage occurrence (see p. 53).

Those plants which occur more commonly or exclusively on the path are those which can withstand trampling; some may be intolerant of much competition. Do any species show special adaptations to either situation?

## VIII. Studies of Animal Life in Special Habitats

1. Animals of cow-dung. If water is available this can be used for bringing dor-beetles *Geotrupes* spp. from their holes under the dung to the surface. Take a jam jar and an old chisel and trowel. Examine patches of different ages.

2. Animals in carcases. Rabbits or other animals can be used. Try several and put them in different habitats. Note the kinds and numbers of animals at the carcases until they are completely disintegrated and dry.

3. Animals of compost heaps, rubbish dumps, etc. There is scope here for investigating seasonal variation.

4. Animals under stones, planks, etc., which can be put out in any desired place. Replace all planks, etc., after examination.

5. Animals of old bird's nests, holes in trees, banks, etc., in hedgerows, bushes and trees, in old ducks' nests, jackdaws' nests in church towers, etc.

6. Animals in nests of mice, voles shrews, etc., and the parasites of these animals (see p. 139).

7. Animals of flood débris (use sieve method, see p. 65).

8. Bird behaviour: e.g. species visiting nesting boxes and feeding tables.

9. Cave animals. A special study of the species of bats and their numbers could be made in a district with a number of caves.

10. Animals associated with growing crops. Pay special attention to the predator-prey relationship. Which are useful and which are harmful species?

11. Animals of stored products (*a*) out of doors, e.g. examine hay ricks, corn stacks, potato clamps, etc., as opportunity arises, (*b*) indoors—corn stores, fruit and bulbs in garden sheds, etc.

12. Animals of special habitats made by man, e.g. a garden, hedge or quarry.

## IX. ESTIMATION OF TOTAL ANIMAL POPULATIONS

Choose a species of which the individuals (1) are easily caught and marked with a small dab of "Joy Brushing Enamel" (yellow, orange, red and blue are conspicuous colours); (2) quickly disperse in the population after being marked; (3) are known to live for at least a few days.

The following are good subjects; isolated colonies should be chosen, for example:

Pond insects; adults of Dytiscid beetles and some Hemiptera (*Notonecta* sp., *Corixa* sp.), colonies of butterflies such as the

Meadow-brown *Maniola jurtina* (L.) and the Chalk-hill Blue *Lysandra coridon* (Poda) and Zygoptera dragonflies.

*Method:* catch a number of specimens and mark them so that each can be easily identified when caught again. A small patch of enamel on a wing, elytron or the thorax is best. Only one colour for each trial must be used. If the enamel will not stick to the scales of a butterfly's wing, rub off a small patch first.

When the marked specimens have mixed with the population catch the same number again. It is best not to do this on the same day, but to wait for a day or two to make certain that the marked specimens are thoroughly dispersed. Note the number of marked specimens in the second catch.

Calculate the populations thus:

$$\frac{\left(\begin{array}{c}\text{Total No. first} \\ \text{caught and marked}\end{array}\right) \times \left(\begin{array}{c}\text{Total No. caught [marked and} \\ \text{unmarked] on second occasion}\end{array}\right)}{\text{(No. of marked specimens of second catch)}}$$

This method does not allow for fluctuations in the population due to death and migration or emergence of fresh adults. It can be used for making annual comparisons of populations in the same area.

REFERENCE

DOWDESWELL, W. H. *Ecology in Secondary Schools*, "Biology in Human Affairs", vol. 19, No. 2, Feb. 1954.

## X. FLIGHT DISTANCES

Many wild animals, especially mammals and birds, allow an enemy to approach to a certain distance—the *flight distance*—before they move away. This distance may differ between individuals of the same species living in different habitats, for example, house sparrows in a town and those on a farm. In some cases a tolerance of man's presence has been acquired, often as a result of food being made available, as anyone with a bird-table knows.

Measure the flight distances of animals as accurately as possible in different places and note where the animals go to. Give the average distance for a number of observations on the same species, and if possible, in different habitats. Can the normal flight distance be reduced by putting out food for any animal?

## XI. QUALITATIVE SAMPLING FOR INVERTEBRATES IN LITTER

Collect a standard quantity of ground litter from as many types of habitat as possible. Use waterproof bags or strong sacks (see p. 69) with a number painted on the outside of each and bring at least 5 lb or $2\frac{1}{2}$ kg by weight of each kind back to the laboratory. Sieve this on to a white surface (see p. 65). This method is useful for teams of workers and can be reserved for a wet day. Classify the animals noting their numbers. Draw up a list in the following way.

| Locality Date | Total numbers | | | | | | | | | | |
|---|---|---|---|---|---|---|---|---|---|---|---|
| | Isopoda | Chelognethi | Acarina | Araneida | Opiliones | Mollusca | Chilopoda | Diplopoda | Collembola | Coleoptera | etc. |
| Beech wood litter (excluding unrotted dry leaves) | 27 | 15 | 6 | 12 | 1 | 14 | 1 | 10 | 16 | 9 | |
| Dogwood scrub with some grass and moss | 68 | 14 | 19 | 10 | 9 | 57 | 6 | 21 | 26 | 6 | |
| Pine-tree litter | 1 | 0 | 5 | 9 | 0 | 0 | 1 | 0 | 11 | 0 | |

The species should be classified in as much detail as possible. If more or less equal samples have been taken and the numbers of animals carefully kept the results will give a rough quantitative idea of the fauna of each habitat. Is it possible to account for any of the differences in species and numbers?

## XII. THE STUDY OF A WOOD

A wood is a plant community in which trees are the most obvious plants. There are a number of features which make the study of woodland plants and animals specially interesting. Woods are admirable for watching the seasonal changes of wild life, and they show particularly well the close association of plants and animals.

Rock-type, soil, climate, altitude, the effects of man and other biotic factors, as well as the species present in the district and which might be available for colonisation, all contribute in determining the type of woodland.

The most conspicuous tree usually gives its name to the wood, for example, oak wood, pine wood, etc. If two trees are about equally conspicuous then, for example, a beech-ash wood is designated.

If the wood is mature and the upper parts of the trees (crowns) touch, and there is a more or less continuous leaf and branch canopy, it is called a *closed* wood, in contrast to an *open* wood, in which the trees are more widely spaced and not touching.

*Special features of woodlands.* 1. By comparison with most other habitats light is considerably reduced.

2. Apart from aquatic or marshy habitats the relative humidity is higher.

3. Because of the breaking effect of the trees there is less wind and the temperature tends to be more constant than in most other habitats.

4. Trees make conditions underneath them unfavourable for the regeneration and growth of many plants. Deciduous woodlands produce a more basic type of humus (*mull*) in which bacteria are the main agents of decay. In coniferous woods there is a more acid humus (*mor*) in which fungi, on or near the surface, are the chief agents of humus decay.

5. Good shelter is provided for some animals, e.g. roosting places for birds and a litter layer for many invertebrates.

*Woodland vegetation* is classified in layers: 1. The Bryophyte layer—mosses and liverworts. Under dense shade one or two species of moss may be the only smaller plants present. Mosses also occur on the bark of trees and on fallen logs. Examples, *Hypnum cupressiforme* Hedw., *Dicranoweissia cirrata* (Hedw.) on the more acidic bark of beech and oak. *Neckera complanata* (Hedw.) and *Isothecium myurum* (Brid.) on the more basic bark of ash, elder and maple. On heavier clay-types of soil *Thuidium tamariscinum* (Hedw.) and *Eurynchium striatum* (Hedw.) are examples whilst *Dicranum majus* Turn. and *Plagiothecium undulatum* (Hedw.) occur on acid soils and *Leucobryum glaucum* (Hedw.) often occurs on acid soils, especially with beech litter.

2. The field layer: this is the herbaceous part of the woodland flora and most of the species have features which serve them well for a woodland existence. Many, like the Primrose *Primula vulgaris* Huds., produce leaves and flowers early in the year, Such plants reproduce and begin to photosynthesise at a period coinciding with the time of maximum of light when the foliage of the trees and shrubs is not yet fully developed. There is a noticeable absence of annuals. Storage organs occur in many species, e.g. Bluebells *Endymion nonscriptus* (L.) which have bulbs, and Wood Spurge *Euphorbia amygdaloides* (L.) which has rhizomes.

In open woodland some of the original species of the sward stage of the succession may be found (see section IV, p. 39).

3. The shrub layer: this is characterised by such familiar plants as Blackberry *Rubus* spp., Honeysuckle *Lonicera periclymemum* (L.) Hazel *Corylus avellana* (L.) Holly *Ilex aquifolium* (L.), etc., together with the younger trees. Many shrubs are dispersed as edible seeds and fruits. Some are evergreens; Honeysuckle produces its foliage very early in the year.

4. The tree layer. Trees produce the bulk of the humus on the woodland floor. Reproduction is chiefly by edible fruits, e.g. Oak, *Quercus* spp. or by special adaptations for wind disposal as in the ash.

*Woodland Animals.* Various kinds of classification are possible, but the scheme outlined on p. 77–(*d*) 1. is useful.

If a long-term study is undertaken there will be marked seasonal differences in the animal life. Diurnal and nocturnal faunas must be studied, even during a short term project. They are usually very different, and may be compared to a day and night shift, both of which contribute to the life of the woodland. Particular attention should be given to the methods of trapping animals (see p. 60), as it is often easier to find some specimens this way than by searching, especially some nocturnal invertebrates. Others, such as woodland butterflies and some Diptera, are most easily recorded on the wing during appropriate weather.

For making permanent records of woodland animals the classification given on p. 77–(d) 1. can be used where appropriate, and under these headings:

1. The soil (direct observation; sampling; flotation; traps).
2. Litter layer (direct observation; sampling in conjunction with Tüllgren funnel and sieving; traps).
3. Field layer (direct observation; sweeping).
4. Shrub layer (direct observation; beating; sugaring).
5. Tree layer (direct observation; beating; sugaring).

Special habitats such as birds' nests, squirrels' dreys, mice nests, bark of trees (inner and outer surfaces), etc., must be examined separately, and parasites and predators must be recorded with their hosts.

*General notes:* the division of the woodland plants into layers (see p. 37) is a convenient basis for descriptive purposes, and for such each layer can be regarded as a community. But the life functions of these are closely connected, and from the trees downwards, each layer exerts a marked physiological effect on the layers below.

On p. 40 it was pointed out that woodland is the natural climax of plant succession over most of Great Britain, but owing to felling, coppicing and planting, and other operations by man, very little natural vegetation now exists. Most woodlands are therefore semi-natural, some entirely so, but this in no way lessens the value and interest of studying them. Coppicing and felling may provide instructive subjects for observation in connection with change in vegetation and fauna.

REFERENCES

NEAL, E. *Woodland Ecology*, William Heinemann Ltd., London, 1953.
CHRYSTAL, R. N. *Insects of the British Woodlands*, Frederick Warne & Co. Ltd., London, 1937.

## XIII. FRESH-WATER LIFE

There is an underlying similarity of habitat in plant and animal life which can be traced in all fresh-water habitats, despite variation in chemical and physical conditions. Modifications of this basic pattern lie between extremes of stagnant waters and swiftly flowing streams and rivers. The studies suggested here are therefore generalised, and the microscopic fauna and flora, though interesting and important, are largely ignored, as fresh-water microscopy is a study in itself.

(1) Consider the special features of fresh-water habitats:

(*i*) Plants and animals do not normally suffer from desiccation.

(*ii*) The temperature of the water does not usually fluctuate widely in a short time; but there may be as much as 20°C difference between summer and winter temperature. Fluctuation is more marked in ponds, and less so in lakes and running water.

(*iii*) The viscosity of water reduces shock so that tough integuments are unnecessary. This is important to plants.

(*iv*) The high density of water (700 times that of air at N.A.P.) increases buoyancy and thus plants, and some animals, do not normally have extensive supporting tissues.

(*v*) Food is usually within easy reach. Salts are dissolved in the surrounding water, but absorption also takes

9

place through the roots of plants. Animals hunt for their food within the prescribed limits of the water, or in streams and lakes, usually within the area of the habitat.

(*vi*) Many small animals, e.g. ciliates, can travel everywhere in the water, and are not confined to a thin film as in the terrestrial habitat; the smaller animals (and plants) often form the food of the larger animals.

(*vii*) There is less oxygen than in a terrestrial habitat; the effects on plants are less important, but animals show modifications to meet this difficulty in two ways:

(*a*) by limitation of size; respiration takes place by simple gaseous diffusion—oxygen from the surrounding water passing in through the body or cell walls, e.g. Protozoa.

(*b*) by adopting special methods; these can be seen particularly well in animals which have taken secondarily to an aquatic existence from the land:

1. *Gills*—increase the surface area through which gaseous exchange takes place; external gills, e.g. young newts and internal gills, e.g. fish.

2. *Rectal gills* of Anisoptera dragonflies; the rectal wall is here folded and richly supplied with tracheae; gaseous exchange takes place through this wall.

3. *Plastron respiration* of some insects. Special hairs on certain parts of the body trap a bubble which functions temporarily as a gill. Its action depends on the faster rate of diffusion of oxygen compared with that of nitrogen. As oxygen is withdrawn from the bubble (through the integument into the tracheal system) the proportion of nitrogen increases, but oxygen from the surrounding water diffuses into the bubble and so into the tracheae, but in decreasing amounts, so that the bubble ultimately has

to be renewed. In insects with this type of respiration the tracheal system is closed (i.e. there are no spiracles), e.g. *Aphelocheirus montandoni* Hor. (Hemiptera).

4. By taking down a bubble of air from above the surface and using this in the same way as terrestrial insects do, through the *open tracheal system*, e.g. Hydrophilid beetles; *Corixa* bugs; *Argyroneta aquatica* (Clerck) the water spider.

5. By taking in air through special structures, e.g. the *respiratory siphon* of *Eristalis* larva the rat-tailed maggot (*Diptera*), and the piercing tubes of some Donacid beetle larvae which utilise the air stored in certain plants below water level.

6. By increasing the intake of oxygen by means of *haemoglobin* in the body, e.g. *Tubifex* (Annelida), larvae of *Chironomus* (Diptera)—blood-worms, and *Planorbis* (Mollusca). Such species often live in ponds and ditches which are stagnant and in which the oxygen content may be low.

(*viii*) Locomotion may demand modified structures for quick movement. In general a paddle is used, e.g. hind legs of *Corixa* bugs. The rectal breathing apparatus of Anisoptera dragonfly larvae can also be used as a locomotory propulsion apparatus. Free floating animals and plants can only live in water in which there is practically no movement.

(*ix*) Reproduction: plants spread mainly by vegetative processes since seed dispersal would be hazardous, hence the presence of large patches of the same species in or by water. There are very few special modifications for reproduction in aquatic animals.

(2) A method of studying fresh-water habitats. First make a general survey.

(*A*) List the plant under—

   (*i*) Those growing in very damp habitats. These are not strictly aquatic, but they should be included, e.g. *Epilobium hirsutum* L. Great Hairy Willowherb. *Filipendula ulmaria* L. Meadowsweet.

   (*ii*) Marginal species, e.g. *Scutellaria galericulata* L. Skullcap, and *Lycopus europaeus* L. Gipsywort.

   (*iii*) Species in the water and fixed to the bottom, e.g. *Nymphaea alba* L. Water Lily, and *Potamogeton* spp. Pondweeds. These plants may be totally submerged or they may have aerial parts.

   (*iv*) Free floating plants, e.g. *Lemna* spp. Duckweeds, and *Hydrochaeris morsus-ranae* L. Frogbit.

(*B*) List the animals under—

   (*i*) Free moving species (*Nekton*)—e.g. fish, water beetles.

   (*ii*) Those which move on a substratum such as mud, stones and plants, and chiefly on or near the bottom (*Benthos*), e.g. leeches (Hirudinea), flatworms (Planaria) dragonfly larvae (Odonata). Burrowing forms—in mud, under stones, etc., may be included.

   (*iii*) Free floating animals (*Plankton*)—less important in fresh-water than in the sea, e.g. some Protozoa, *Daphnia* (water flea), etc.

   (*iv*) Those associated with the surface film (*Neuston*)— e.g. *Gerris* spp. (pondskaters), *Gyrinus* spp. (whirligig beetles) on top, and Culicid larvae (Diptera) underneath.

   (*v*) Those associated with the water, but not actually in it, or on it, all the time (*Associates*)—e.g. water birds, frog, adult dragonflies, house martins and swallows feeding over the surface. Some of these may be important biotic factors in the habitat.

The marginal plants may occasionally become submerged when the water level rises, and a leech will sometimes become free swimming, though it is not normally a member of the nekton fauna. There may be some overlap between the previously mentioned categories, but this method of recording is useful, as it gives an indication of the habitats of the plants, and the ways of life of the animals and their relationship to their environment. With careful observation and the use of literature, it should be possible to assign the plants and animals of any aquatic habitat to these categories. Sub-divisions of these can be introduced as required, for example, in a swiftly flowing stream species clinging to stones would be placed in a special division of the benthos.

If the survey is continued at different times of the year which if possible should be done, indicate which of the plants are (1) annuals, (2) biennials and (3) perennials, and which animals are (1) carnivores, including parasites, (2) herbivores and (3) omnivores.

Observations on a fresh-water aquarium, especially on the feeding habits of certain animals, may be instructive. Details of the management of all types of aquaria will be found in many books, magazines and pamphlets. (See School Nature Study, vol. 51, no. 202, p. 1, 1956).

References: See p. 154.

## Section H

# APPENDICES

### I. THE MEASUREMENT OF pH (See p. 15)

There are a number of methods which differ in their degree of accuracy.

1. On p. 119 will be found a list of some plants which are indicative of basic and acid soils. Here is a close link between Botany and Pedology, and knowledge of a few indicator plants can be very helpful to the field biologist.

2. A bottle of dilute hydrochloric acid is useful in the field. A small quantity is poured on the soil to be tested. If calcareous it will fizz when the acid and base react giving off carbon dioxide. If it does not fizz the soil is acid or neutral.

3. The B.D.H. Universal Soil Testing Indicator (supplied by British Drug Houses Ltd.) is helpful for more accurate and quick tests in the field. The liquid is neutral (pH 7), and is a mixture of indicators each with a different range of pH. The set is supplied with a small trough and spatula. The trough must be clean before using. If it is not possible to wash it, rub it out with some of the soil to be tested. Avoid making contact between the soil and any part of the skin, as the products of one's sweat glands may give an acid reaction.

Place a small quantity of the soil in the larger end of the trough, and pour on enough indicator to give a slight excess. After about one minute pour the excess liquid over into the small end of the trough, and read the pH, either by a colour comparison with a chart, or according to the following:

116

no change in colour—soil is neutral,
bluish tinge—basic,
yellow colour—slightly acid,
orange colour—moderately acid,
red colour—very acid.

4. Indicators can be used separately with a colour chart for comparison. A spot testing plate is normally used.
Examples are:

Bromothymol blue—pH range    6–7·6
Chlorophenol red —     „      4·6–7
Bromocresol green—      „      3·6–5·2

5. A more accurate result is given by the B.D.H. capillator. Used on the same principle as the Universal outfit, a close colour comparison is made with a standard set of indicators. For this purpose the solution, prepared by adding the indicator to the soil in a small watch glass, is drawn up in a capillary tube. The set of standard colours each of known pH value in capillary tubes is calibrated to read at intervals of 0·2.

One of the chief difficulties in making accurate colour comparisons in soil tests, is the presence of the clay fraction which, even if slight, remains in suspension in the liquid. To clear it a floculating substance, such as barium sulphate, is used. A complete outfit is supplied by British Drug Houses Ltd.

6. The most accurate pH determination depends for its working on electrode potentials, a discussion of which will be found in any text-book of physical chemistry. Briefly, an aqueous extract of the soil is made to act as part of the electrolyte in a battery. The voltage of this battery varies according to the concentration of $H^+$ ions in the soil water used, and measurement of this voltage is used to calculate the pH value. Commercial instruments, known as pH meters, work upon this principle and are calibrated directly in pH instead of volts.

## II. Key to the Identification of Soils *

### (See p. 18.)

Allowance must be made for a soil which is very wet or very dry.

*I.* Soil gritty (without being sticky) . . . . . A
*II.* Soil sticky and/or silky (without being gritty) . . . B
*III.* Soil sticky and gritty . . . . . . . C
*IV.* Soil not gritty, nor silky, nor sticky . . . LOAM (1)

A   (*a*) Can be formed into a cohesive ball

    1. Soil particles of type (sea-shore) size   SANDY LOAM (2)
    2. Particles markedly coarser than 1  COARSE SANDY LOAM (3)
    3. Particles markedly finer than 1 .   FINE SANDY LOAM (4)
    4. Particles barely visible to naked eye
                  VERY FINE SANDY LOAM (5)

   (*b*) Cannot be formed into a cohesive ball . (*aa*) or (*bb*)

    (*aa*) Does not soil clean skin

      1. Soil particles of type (sea-shore size) . . SAND (6)
      2. Particles markedly coarser than 1   COARSE SAND (7)
      3. Particles markedly finer than 1 . . FINE SAND (8)
      4. Particles barely visible to naked eye . VERY FINE SAND (9)

    (*bb*) Soils clean skin

      1. Particles of type (sea-shore) size . LOAMY SAND (10)
      2. Particles markedly coarser than 1 LOAMY COARSE SAND (11)
      3. Particles markedly finer than 1 . LOAMY FINE SAND (12)
      4. Particles barely visible to naked eye
                  LOAMY VERY FINE SAND (13)

B   (*a*) Cannot be polished between fingers

    1. Clearly silky . . . . . SILT LOAM (14)
    2. Not clearly silky . . . . SILTY LOAM (15)

   (*b*) Can be polished between fingers

    1. Easily deformed . . . SILTY CLAY LOAM (16)
    2. Deformed with difficulty . . . CLAY LOAM (17)
    3. Very resistant . . . . . . CLAY (18)

C   1. Cannot be polished between fingers SANDY SILT LOAM (19)
   2. Can be polished between fingers SANDY CLAY LOAM (20)

* The number in brackets after each soil is given for quick reference in the field note-book, for example, instead of writing Silty Clay Loam, 16 is quoted.

III. SOME IMPORTANT CALCICOLE AND CALCIFUGE PLANTS

The following list indicates the more important plants whose distribution appears to be governed by a high (*calcicoles*) or a low (*calcifuges*) base status of the soil. The range of these plants within the British Isles is given in standard floras.

## Calcicoles

*Acrocladium cuspidatum* (Hedw.) a moss
*Anthyllis vulneraria* L. Kidney Vetch
*Asperula cynanchica* L. Squinancywort
*Asplenium trichomanes* L. Maindenhair Spleenwort, a fern
*A. viride* Huds. a fern
*Blackstonia perfoliata* (L.) Yellow-wort
*Brachypodium pinnatum* (L.) False-brome Grass
*Bromus erectus* Huds. Upright-brome Grass
*Campanula glomerata* L. Clustered Bell-flower
*Camptothecium lutescens* (Hedw.) a moss
*Carex lepidocarpa* Tausch Long-stalked Yellow Sedge
*Cephalanthera damasonium* (Mill.) White Helleborine
*Cirsium acaule* (L.) Stemless Thistle
*Clematis vitalba* L. Traveller's Joy
*Clinopodium vulgare* L. Wild Basil
*Cornus sanguinea* L. Dogwood
*Ctenidium molluscum* (Hedw.) a moss
*Cystopteris fragilis* (L.) a fern
*Daphne laureola* L. Spurge Laurel
*Erigeron acris* L. Blue Fleabane
*Euonymus europaeus* L. Spindle
*Filipendula vulgaris* Moench. Dropwort
*Galium pumilum* Murr. Slender Bedstraw
*Gentianella amarella* (L.) Felwort
*Gymnadenia conopsea* (L.) Fragrant Orchid
*Helianthemum chamaecistus* Mill. Common Rockrose
*Hippocrepis comosa* L. Horse-shoe Vetch
*Inula conyza* DC Ploughman's Spikenard
*Juncus subnodulosus* Schrank Blunt-flowered Rush

*Koeleria gracilis* Pers. Crested Hair-grass
*Linum catharticum* L. Purging Flax
*Neckera crispa* Hedw. a moss
*Ophrys apifera* Huds. Bee Orchid
*O. insectifera* L. Fly Orchid
*Origanum vulgare* L. Marjoram
*Paris quadrifolia* L. Herb Paris
*Polystichum lonchitis* (L.) Holly Fern
*Poterium sanguisorba* L. Salad Burnet
*Primula veris* L. Cowslip
*Scabiosa columbaria* L. Small Scabius
*Sesleria caerulea* Scop. Blue Sesleria
*Tortella tortuosa* (Hedw.) a moss
*Viburnum lantana* L. Wayfaring Tree
*Viola hirta* L. Hairy Violet

Calcifuges

*Agrostis tenuis* Sibth. Common Bent Grass
*Blechnum spicant* (L.) Hard Fern
*Calluna vulgaris* (L.) Ling
*Carex binervis* Sm. Ribbed Sedge
*C. ovalis* Good. Oval Sedge
*C. echinata* Murr Star Sedge
*Deschampsia flexuosa* (L.) Wavy Hair Grass
*Digitalis purpurea* L. Foxglove
*Drosera rotundifolia* L. Sundew
*Empetrum nigrum* L. Crowberry
*Erica tetralix* L. Cross-leaved Heather
*E. cinerea L.* Bell Heather
*Eriophorum vaginatum* L. Hare's Tail
*Galium hercynicum* Weigel Heath Bedstraw
*Genista anglica* L. Petty Whin
*Juncus acutiflorus* Hoffm. Sharp-flowered Rush
*J. squarrosus* L. Heath Rush
*Molinia caerulea* (L.) Purple Moor Grass
*Narthecium ossifragum* (L.) Bog Asphodel
*Orchis ericetorum* E.F.L. Heath-spotted Orchid

*Oxycoccus palustris* Pers. Cranberry
*Pedicularis sylvatica* L. Lousewort
*Pleurozium schreberi* (Brid.) a moss
*Polytrichum commune* Hedw. a moss
*Potentilla erecta* (L.) Common Tormentil
*Pteridium aquilinum* (L.) Bracken
*Rhynchospora alba* (L.) White Beak-sedge
*Rhododendron ponticum* L.
*Rumex acetosella* L. Sheep's Sorrel
*Sphagnum* spp. Bog mosses
*Ulex gallii* Planch. Western Gorse
*U. minor* Roth. Dwarf Furze
*Vaccinium myrtillus* L. Bilberry.

## IV. PRESERVING PLANTS

Whenever possible all parts of a plant, including the roots, should be taken. Care and discretion must be used when collecting uncommon species.

### Pressing

Use coarse quality newspaper and an old trouser press, or pile of books. Arrange the parts of the plant carefully, as far as possible displaying the essential features. Thick parts, such as the flower heads of thistles, can be cut vertically, and one half pressed. Include full field data with each specimen. Stick the specimens on to good quality white paper when they are pressed and dry. The standard size paper used at Kew is $10\frac{1}{2} \times 16\frac{1}{2}$ in. ($27 \times 42$ cm). Specimens may be attached by small strips of gummed white paper or by a synthetic plastic such as "Bexol". Adhesive transparent materials are not recommended. Write the name and field data on each sheet.

Pressing can also be done with an iron. This should be hot, but not so hot as to scorch. Do not rub the iron along, but place it vertically down on the specimen from place to place. A single sheet of newspaper should be placed between the specimen and the iron. Plants treated in this way should be left to dry for a day before they are mounted. This is a good method for flat plants such as grasses, sedges and ferns.

Some fruits and seeds and woody parts of plants cannot be preserved in this way. It is best to make drawings of these.

### Drying

Applicable to mosses, lichens and some fruits and seeds. Mosses and lichens are left to dry. They are then put in envelopes or folded pieces of paper; the name and other data are written on the outside, and the collection can be kept like a card index. Mosses can be examined by moistening them, when they become soft and show their original characters.

A few fungi can be dried, but it is impossible to preserve most species satisfactorily. Good drawings and paintings, as well as photographs, are useful.

Use P.D.B. (see p. 136) for keeping the herbarium free from pests.

*Note:* plants are often collected in a *vasculum* made for the purpose. Provided that not too many specimens are put in it, they will survive in a fresh condition, and will not get muddled or damaged. Tins are a good substitute for a vasculum and smaller ones, as well as envelopes and Polythene bags, can be used for mosses and lichens.

Larger plants can also be collected and pressed in newspaper between two metal grids strapped together. This is a satisfactory method, but the press must be kept out of rain.

### V. NOMENCLATURE AND CLASSIFICATION

The field biologist who deals with a large number of species of plants and animals must use the correct scientific names. This section explains why most animals and plants have two scientific names, and why it is desirable to use the most modern name of a species. The more important points made by the International Commissions of Zoological and Botanical Nomenclature are mentioned. Emminent zoologists and botanists from many countries sit on these Commissions, which publish their *Codes* from time to time. These Codes deserve careful attention by all students of biology, since they are intended to secure stability of nomenclature, and to avoid mistakes and misunderstandings about scientific names.

Every plant and animal is known internationally by two scientific names. The first or *generic name* is written with an initial capital letter, the second or *specific* (= *trivial*) name should be written with a small initial letter. The scientific names, sometimes referred to as the *proper names*, are followed by the name of the author, often abbreviated, who first described the species, and with NO intervening comma, e.g. *Mus musculus* Linné—the House Mouse.

If the species has been transferred from the genus under which it was originally described, to a new genus, the author's name should appear in brackets, e.g. *Oryctolagus cuniculus* (Linné)—the Rabbit.

In such cases, and especially when the old generic name is widely known, it may be convenient to quote the alternative generic name. This is done either by placing it in round brackets preceded by an equals sign, or by placing it in square brackets e.g. *Pygosteus* (= *Gasterosteus*) *pungitius* (Linné) or *Pygosteus* [*Gasterosteus*] *pungitius* Linné—the Ten-spined Stickleback.

Three names are used to denote a sub-species. The sub-specific name follows the specific name, and the author quoted is the one who first described the sub-species, e.g. *Corvus monedula spermologus* Viellot—the Jackdaw.

The only valid generic or specific name of an animal or plant is the one published nearest, but not previous, to 1758—the year of publication of the tenth edition of Linné's *Systema Natura*. There are a few minor exceptions to this. If an author publishes a name for an animal or plant, and it is later found that the species has already been described under another name, then, according to the *Law of Priority* the older name— provided it is not previous to 1758—is the only valid one, and should be adopted. In certain cases of well-established and familiar names, the International Commissions allow exceptions to the Law of Priority, and such names remain valid.

Lists of groups of animals and plants are called *catalogues*. After the name and author of each species in a catalogue, it is customary to give the date, usually the year, when a description of the species was published.

IT IS ALWAYS PREFERABLE TO USE SCIENTIFIC NAMES. IN SOME GROUPS LIKE BUTTERFLIES, BIRDS AND FLOWERING PLANTS, THE ENGLISH NAMES MAY BE QUOTED AS WELL. VERNACULAR, I.E. COMMON, POPULAR OR ENGLISH NAMES, HAVE BEEN APPLIED TO MANY SPECIES. THESE NAMES ARE SOMETIMES USED LOCALLY, DIFFERENT ONES BEING EMPLOYED IN ANOTHER PART OF THE COUNTRY, AND THEY ARE OFTEN MEANINGLESS AND ARE INTERNATIONALLY USELESS. (For the derivation of scientific names see bibliography, p. 156).

The following terms are sometimes used in taxonomic works. (*Taxonomy* is that branch of biology concerned with the recognition, description, nomenclature and classification of plants and animals):

*Type specimen*—this is the specimen or one of the specimens which an author used to describe a new species. If there is only one specimen it is a *holotype*; if several these are *syntypes*. An author may subsequently select one of the syntypes as the type; this is called the *lectotype* and the remaining syntypes become *paratypes*.

Animals and plants are classified according to the system of the eighteenth century biologist Carl von Linné (often latinised to Linnaeus). This system is in universal use. The arrangement of species, genera, families and "higher" groups, is supposed to show an evolutionary relationship, so far as present knowledge permits. Most of the classification of the major groups of animals and plants is undisputed, but biologists are not always in agreement over the arrangement of species, genera and families. For example Mammals have evolved from Reptiles, and Reptiles from Amphibia and Amphibia from fish. The order of classification starting from the "highest" animals is therefore *Mammalia, Reptilia, Amphibia, Pisces*. This is a *natural classification*. But in the genus *Phyllotreta*—flea bettles —(which are well-known pests of *Brassica* crops), it is not possible to classify all the species in an evolutionary series. They are therefore grouped together according to convenience —often in such cases to facilitate identification of the species. This is an *artificial classification*. Parallel cases occur in the plant kingdom.

The chief divisions of the animal and plant kingdoms are given here, with examples of the Common Frog *Rana temporana* Linné and Dog Rose, *Rosa canina* Linné.

PHYLUM: CORDATA
SUB-PHYLUM: VERTEBRATA
CLASS: AMPHIBIA
ORDER: SALIENTA
FAMILY: RANIDAE
GENUS: *Rana*
SPECIES: *temporaria* Linné

DIVISION: SPERMATOPHYTA
CLASS: ANGIOSPERMAE
ORDER: ROSALES
FAMILY: ROSACEAE
GENUS: *Rosa*
SPECIES: *canina* Linné

Further divisions of any of the preceding may be used, e.g. sub-order, tribe, series, etc., but these are rarely employed consistently by systematists. A large genus may be split into sub-genera, and a species into a number of sub-species. A recognised variety is designated by the prefix "var" ( = variety), e.g. the pale form of the female *Colias croceus* (Geoff.) var. *helice*, the Clouded Yellow Butterfly.

When a species of plant is variable, but groups showing certain similarities are recognisable, the term *aggregate* is used, e.g. *Thymus serpyllum* agg.

*Note:* when written or typed, scientific names should always be underlined. In printing it is customary to use italics for the genus and species; higher groups may or may not be printed in italics. When a genus is quoted, but the species is not specified, the abbreviation *sp.* (plural *spp.*) should be given, e.g. *Ranunculus* sp.

Most of the standard zoological and botanical text-books contain information on classification and nomenclature. These should be consulted, e.g. Wengon's *Protozoology* and Dawe's Round discs and triangles for Diptera, etc., can be bought, as

*The Trematoda.* Reports are also issued by the International Commission on Nomenclature already mentioned.

## VI. IDENTIFICATION OF INVERTEBRATES

Because of the importance, large number, and difficulty in naming many invertebrates, identification is sometimes only possible to the order, family or genus. Though specific identification should be made when possible, group determination will often suffice for general survey purposes.

For a general introduction to Invertebrates the bibliography should be consulted (see p. 153). The present notes are intended to assist in the separation of members of certain groups which are superficially alike, and which are widespread and common. Only the more important field characters are mentioned.

### *Phylum* ARTHROPODA.

*Segmented animals* with *paired limbs* and at least *one pair of jaws*; the *cuticle* is *chitinous* and forms the *exoskeleton*.

#### *Class* Chilopoda (Centipedes).

Typical body segment, i.e. one in the middle of the body, has one pair of legs; flattened dorso-ventrally; all are carnivorous and move rapidly when disturbed.

#### *Class* Diplopoda (Millipedes).

Typical body segment with two pairs of legs; rounded (except in Polydesmidae), all are herbivorous, and coil up like a watch-spring when disturbed.

*Notes:* the class Myriapoda of older systematists is now divided into the two classes Chilopoda and Diplopoda.

The "pill millipede" *Glomeris marginata* (Villers) should not be confused with the "pill woodlouse" Genus *Armadillidium* (7 British spp. class Crustacea, Order Isopoda). The distinctions are made clear in figs. 40 and 41.

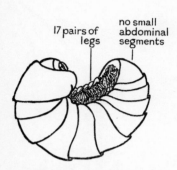

FIG. 40.—*Glomeris* sp. The Pill-
millipede, lateral, × 7

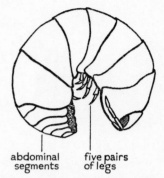

FIG. 41.—*Armadillidium* sp. The
Pill-woodlouse, lateral, × 14

*Class* Insecta.

Body divisible into *head, thorax* and *abdomen*; three
pairs of legs in adult; *wings* usually present. Except
for a few primitive insects all have a *life-cycle* or *metamorphosis*. *Antennae* present.

*Order* Hemiptera (Plant Bugs).

Mouth parts suctorial, piercing plant tissues (with
few exceptions which are blood suckers) and with-
drawing sap by means of *rostrum* (fig. 42). *Forewings*
(*elytra* or *hemi-elytra*) never completely hardened,
(fig. 43). Some members of the sub-order Heteroptera
may be confused with Coleoptera (Beetles).

*Order* Coleoptera (Beetles).

Mouth parts biting (*mandibles*) (fig. 44). Elytra evenly
hardened throughout.

*Note:* the "rostrum" of the Weevil beetles (Curculionidae)
should not be confused with the rostrum of the Hemiptera.
In Weevils this is merely an elongated part of the head and
bears mandibles at the tip.

10

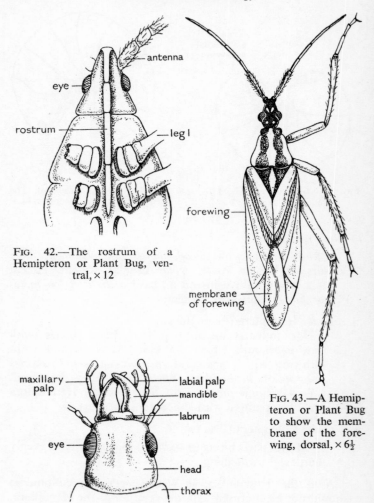

FIG. 42.—The rostrum of a Hemipteron or Plant Bug, ventral, × 12

FIG. 43.—A Hemipteron or Plant Bug to show the membrane of the forewing, dorsal, × 6½

FIG. 44.—Mouth parts of a Coleopteron (Beetle) dorsal, × 10

*Order* Hymenoptera (Ants, Bees, Wasps, Ichneumons, Sawflies, etc.).

Two pairs of wings (these may be closely united so that careful examination is necessary). Front part of abdomen constricted into a *pedicel*, except in Symphyta (Sawflies). Antennae usually long (fig. 45).

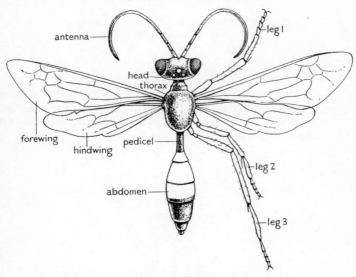

FIG. 45.—A Hymenopteron, dorsal, × 5½

*Note:* many Hymenoptera have some powerful weapon of offence or defence and bear aposematic colours (see p. 102). Some Diptera mimic Hymenoptera and the distinction of members of these groups is often important.

The larvae of Sawflies, which have at least six pairs of *prolegs* (fig. 46), should not be confused with those of some Lepidoptera (Butterflies and Moths) in which the larvae, excepting the Hepialidae (Swift moths), never possess more than five pairs of prolegs.

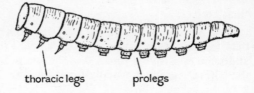

FIG. 46.—Larva of a Sawfly (Hymenoptera; Symphyta), lateral, × 4

*Order* Diptera (Flies).

One pair of wings. The *halteres* which are the remains of the hindwings look like minute tennis rackets, one behind each wing. Antennae usually short (fig. 47). All larvae (grubs) are legless (apodous).

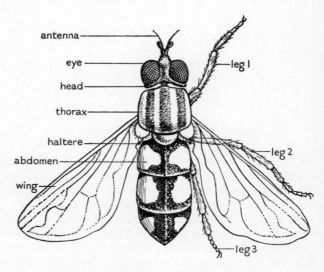

FIG. 47.—A Dipteron or true Fly, dorsal, × 6

*Class* Arachnida.

Body divided into (anterior) *cephalothorax* and (posterior) *abdomen*; four pairs of walking legs in adult; no wings.

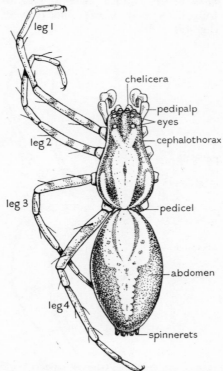

FIG. 48.—An Araneid or true Spider, dorsal, × 7

*Order* Araneida (= Araneae) (Spiders).

Two parts of body joined by a *pedicel*, eyes usually 4, 6 or 8; male (*pedi*) *palps* clubbed. Second pair of legs not usually the longest. All can produce silk, but not all make webs (fig. 48).

*Order* Opiliones ( = Phalangida) (Harvest-spiders, Harvestmen).

Two parts of body united right across; eyes always 2; *palps* never clubbed. Second pair of legs always the longest. No *silk glands*. *Anal opening* a horizontal slit (fig. 49).

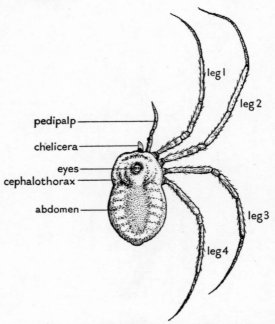

FIG. 49.—An Opilionid (Harvest-spider), dorsal, × 6

*Order* Acarina ( = Acari) (Mites, Ticks, Harvesters).

Very variable; all small (except ticks gorged with blood). Boundary between *cephalothorax* and *abdomen* dorsally obscure; no *external segmentation*; *anal aperture* a vertical slit.

## VII. Preserving Invertebrates

These notes are intended only as a guide to elementary museum techniques complementary to field work. For further details reference should be made to the bibliography (see p. 154, IX, 3 and p. 155, XI, 2).

If specimens are intended for dissection, or for sectioning, special fixatives are normally used, and the relevant literature should be consulted.

For museum specimens which will be used for external examination and dissection of genitalia, the following methods are suggested:

### Key to abbreviations

A  indicates that specimens are preserved by putting them direct into industrial methylated spirit (I.M.S.) (see p. 134).

G  indicates that specimens are gummed on to Bristol board (see p. 134).

P  indicates that specimens are pinned with special entomological pins (see p. 135), but not set.

PS  the same as P but specimens are also set (see p. 135).

ea  indicates that ethyl acetate is used as a killing agent (see p. 137).

pc  indicates that potassium cyanide is the killing agent (see p. 136).

hw  hot water is used for killing.

l   = larva.

/   indicates and/or.

### Insects

| | | | |
|---|---|---|---|
| 1. Apterygota | A | | |
| 2. Orthoptera | G/P/PS | ea/pc | l = G/P/PS |
| 3. Dermaptera | A/G | ea | l = A/G |
| 4. Plecoptera | PS | pc | l = A |
| 5. Psocoptera | A | | |
| 6. Anoplura | A | | |
| 7. Ephemeroptera | PS | pc | l = A |
| 8. Odonata | PS | ea/pc | l = A |

| | | | |
|---|---|---|---|
| 9. Thysanoptera | A | | |
| 10. Hemiptera | G/P/PS | ea/hw | 1 = G/P/PS/A Aphids and very young forms are best made into slides or A |
| 11. Neuroptera | PS | ea/pc | 1 = A |
| 12. Mecoptera | PS | ea/pc | 1 = A |
| 13. Trichoptera | PS | ea/pc | 1 = A |
| 14. Lepidoptera | PS | pc | 1 = A or dry (blown)* |
| 15. Coleoptera | P/PS/G | ea/hw | 1 = A |
| 16. Strepsiptera | A | | |
| 17. Hymenoptera | P/PS/G/A | ea/pc | 1 = A (sawflies can be blown)* |
| 18. Diptera | P/PS | ea/pc | 1 = A |
| 19. Aphaniptera | A | or slides | |

Where there is no special method indicated for the preservation of larvae, they should be treated in the same way as the adults. All other invertebrates are usually put direct into 70% I.M.S. Some, such as millipedes, can first be killed for examination by placing them in a Petri dish on the lid of which a few drops of glacial acetic acid have been placed. This usually causes them to die with their limbs outstretched.

*Notes:*—I.M.S. (often called "alcohol") can be bought at chemists or from chemical dealers by anyone with the necessary licence. The latter is obtainable, free of charge, from the local Customs and Excise authority. The spirit is about 95%. To dilute it to 70%, add 32 parts of water to a 100 of I.M.S. Add a drop (*only a drop*) of glycerine to prevent the specimens becoming too hard. Surgical spirit and formalin are used only in special cases, and on the whole are best avoided as preservatives.

*Bristol Board.* Paste board or cardboard will NOT do, it curls and becomes discoloured. Use three-ply Bristol board for the smaller cards, and four- or six-ply for the larger pieces.

* See bibliography, p. 154, IX, nos. 1 and 3.

Round discs and triangles for Diptera, etc., can be bought, as well as card with standard sizes marked on it. A stock of different size cards can be cut to order fairly cheaply at stationers. Cellulose is sometimes used in place of Bristol board.

*Gum:* powdered (NOT lump) gums Tragacanth and Arabic, half and half, are made to a cream with slightly diluted formalin, or dilute corrosive sublimate solution (mercuric chloride),* to prevent mould. Use a fine "camel-hair" brush, and as little gum as possible. The gum is invisible when it dries. A moderately thick solution of cellulose chips, dissolved in amyl acetate or acetone, is used for gumming specimens to cellulose.

*Pins:* methods P and PS. Always use entomological pins—preferably black. Put the pin through the thorax (in the side in smaller Diptera) or through one elytron in the larger Coleoptera and Hemiptera. Micro-pins are mounted in polyporus strips (see p. 136) which are themselves pinned with entomological pins. The wings and limbs can be set out if necessary. In specimens in which the wings are an essential feature for identification, as in Lepidoptera, special cork setting boards are used. Each has a central groove into which the body fits. The wings are moved forward and held down by strips of paper. The antennae, and in the moths the front pair of legs, are pinned out. It is preferable to use a flat setting board. The specimens are allowed to dry slowly for seven days, or longer, with larger specimens. If they are dried artificially do not put them in an oven, the wings are liable to curl. A gentle heat such as an airing cupboard is better.

When dry, all pins, except that in the thorax, are removed and the insects are transferred to the collection.

*Important:* a small piece of paper on which is written the place of capture, date, collector's initials or name, etc., should be placed, in each tube of spirit, attached to each pinned insects; these data should be written under each piece of Bristol board.

*Relaxing:* for setting it is essential to have insects properly relaxed. Relaxing can be done over moist sand in a tin, or in a

* POISON!

jar into which very young shoots of the Cherry Laurel, *Prunus laurocerasus* L., chopped and bruised, have been put. This can be used as a killing bottle for a time, but after the hydrocyanic acid gas has gone, it remains an excellent relaxing jar for some time. When making such a jar it is advisable to do so out of doors, as the fumes given off are poisonous.

*Para-dichlorobenzene* (P.D.B. obtainable at chemists) is a good preventative against pests which destroy dried specimens. Most store-cases and cabinet drawers have special recesses into which this is put. Failing these, small muslin bags containing the P.D.B., and kept in position by a pin, can be used. They must be renewed from time to time.

### VIII. MAKING *POLYPORUS* STRIPS FOR MOUNTING INSECTS

*Polyporus betulinus* Fr., the Birch bracket fungus, is found on dead or moribund parts of Birch trees (*Betula* spp.). It grows out horizontally from the wood, and is brownish on top, and white below with numerous very small pore-like gills.

Choose large fresh specimens. Remove the gills and dark skin, and cut the block into about six convenient sizes, each as long as possible. Allow these to dry slowly for a few days; an airing cupboard is a good place for this. Finally cut each block into long strips $\frac{1}{10}$ in. (3 mm) square. Put these in a tin with a few crystals of Thymol or P.D.B. (see above), to destroy any beetle grubs, or other pests which may have hatched from eggs laid in the fungus.

Polyporus is best cut on glass with a sharp razor blade against a straight metal or glass edge. All the glass or metal as well as one's fingers should be clean, as the strips readily pick up dirt.

### IX. KILLING BOTTLES
See p. 133

(*A*) Cyanide bottles.

**Potassium and sodium cyanide are poisons. They are obtainable** (at chemists) **only by persons over 21.** Used in killing bottles they are safe if handled by young persons with common sense.

How to make a cyanide bottle.

(*i*) Get a *strong* glass or plastic jar with a tight-fitting rubber or cork bung (screw-on caps are not recommended).

(*ii*) Some dental or commercial plaster of Paris.

(*iii*) 2 oz. (60 grams, or more according to the number of bottles needed) of lump potassium or sodium cyanide.

*Method:* Put a thin layer ($\frac{1}{2}$ in. or 10 mm) of dry plaster of Paris in the jar. Place the cyanide on this (2 oz. or 60 grams per jar). Make a mixture of plaster of Paris and water so that it runs fairly easily. Pour it at once on to the cyanide so as to cover this completely. The jar should now be about one-third filled.

The fumes of hydrocyanic acid gas given off by the cyanide are poisonous. It is therefore best to do this operation in a well-ventilated place. Leave the killing bottle to dry with the bung off for twenty-four hours but put it—and always keep it— in a safe place.

The law requires the bottle to be labelled POISON (French, *poison*; German, *Gift*), and when not in use it must be kept in a locked cupboard.

Never leave a killing bottle in the direct rays of the sun or in a hot place. The time it lasts depends on how much it is used. If the bung is always firmly replaced a bottle should last two seasons.

The old plaster and cyanide can usually be removed by gentle chipping, after preliminary softening with hot water, or with a mixture of nitric and hydrochloric acid (CARE! do this out of doors). If the contents cannot be removed, and the bottle has to be abandoned, it must be disposed of with caution, for example, it can be well buried in the ground.

(*B*) Asphyxiating bottles—for use with ethyl acetate and other liquid killing agents.

(*i*) Any strong glass container with a good fitting bung.

(*ii*) A piece of sponge (artificial or natural).

*Method:* fit about half an inch or 10 mm of the sponge at the bottom of the bottle. This will act as a "reservoir" for the killing agent. A small container of the killing fluid should be taken on long expeditions, so that the bottle can be recharged when necessary.

## X. How to send Small Animals through the Post

Many specimens will travel alive, e.g. beetles, snails and spiders. They should be packed so as not to be jolted about too much, but at the same time they should be free to move. If they require moisture, leaves or moss will usually suffice to supply this. Aquatic animals can usually be sent in moist pond weed or moss.

Dry and brittle preserved specimens must not be jarred. If they are pinned, the cork in the container should be deep, and the box should be well wrapped round with corrugated cardboard to absorb knocks. If specimens are sent folded in pieces of paper, these should be put in a strong box, or tin, so that they will not rattle, but they must not be pressed in tightly.

Specimens preserved in 70% Industrial methylated spirit should be sent in strong tubes, with properly fitting corks or stoppers. Put in the minimum amount of spirit to keep the specimen(s) moist, and also a little tissue paper to prevent their becoming damaged through movement.

## XI. Cleaning Skulls and Bones

It is often useful to have a reference collection of skulls and bones to provide evidence of the presence of species, and for identification in analyses of bird pellets, stomach contents, etc.

The best results are obtained from fresh specimens. First remove as much fur or feathers as possible. Gently simmer the carcase in water to which has been added a small quantity of *pancreatin* (obtainable from chemists). If the water is neutral (see p. 116) add a very small quantity of washing soda, or any alkaline substance, such as one of the well-known brands of stomach powders.

Pancreatin is an enzyme acting only in alkaline solution, it digests the muscle and gristle, after which the bone is left clean. Skulls and bones can be washed under the tap after treatment. The brain is usually soft enough to pour out. To whiten the skull and bones gently boil them in hydrogen peroxide; (20 vol.); immerse them in alcohol for a few minutes and allow to dry (the peroxide and alcohol can be used more than once).

Care must be taken with delicate specimens such as shrews and small birds. Only experience will determine the times necessary for treatment in the pancreatin solution and peroxide. The specimens should be put in the saucepan in a smaller container, made of gauze or perforated zinc, so that they do not touch the bottom. This precaution should not be omitted as otherwise the specimens are likely to become discoloured, and this cannot be remedied by peroxide treatment. The loss of small bones and teeth is also minimised.

## XII. Collecting External Parasites of Birds and Mammals

*Apparatus:* Tubes of 70% alcohol (see p. 134); small brush; dissecting forceps; bottle of chloroform; paper bags.

Avoid unduly frightening wild animals and do not injure them. Speed and precision must be used to pick off parasites. If they cling, or if their mouth parts are embedded in the skin, a drop of chloroform usually causes them to release their hold. Search in and behind the ears of mammals, and under the belly, especially near the legs. Bird parasites are often congregated under the wings close to the body and round the neck. On bats they occur anywhere in the fur.

Animals which are obtained dead must be very fresh or the parasites will have left the body. Put the latter into a paper bag and pour in a few drops of chloroform. Examine the the contents after a few minutes; the parasites will have dropped to the bottom of the bag.

## XIII. How to give a Grid Reference

Modern Ordnance maps are divided into squares (The Grid System). The N.–S. vertical lines are numbered left to right; the W.–E. horizontal ones are numbered from the bottom to the top of the map.

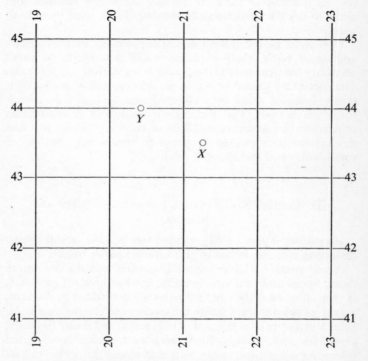

To give the grid reference to a point *X* in the diagram read the number of the line on the west edge of the square in which the position lies, i.e. begin by reading the numbers as you would a book (note that these numbers are usually printed vertically). We now have 21. Measure in tenths from this line to *X*, that is towards the next line on the right of *X*. In the above example it is $\frac{3}{10}$ (i.e. $\frac{3}{10}$ of the way from line 21 to 22). This gives 213.

Next read the number of the line on the S. edge of the square, i.e. 43, and measure the tenths northwards (upwards) to $X$. This reads 435.

The full grid reference to $X$ is now written as 213435.

Where a point lies on a line the reference is "0", e.g. the point $Y$ on diagram would read as 204440.

Where a more precise reference is needed, each tenth can again be subdivided into tenths, and so an eight figure reference is obtained, e.g. 21354353.

### XIV. KEEPING WEATHER RECORDS

Methods of weather recording, standards used and apparatus needed, are given in the Air Ministry's *Observer's Handbook*, Meteorological Office, M.O.554(1956).

The Meteorological Office assists with local weather recording by loaning apparatus to *bone fide* applicants. Details of this scheme may be had from the address given in the footnote on p. 10.

It is not always possible, or necessary, to set up a permanent recording station; records of the wind or rainfall only, for example, may be needed.

Recordings are made by instruments or by description.

*Descriptive Recordings*

  *i.* General weather
  *ii.* Cloud
  *iii.* Visibility
  *iv.* Wind

*Recording by Instruments*

  *v.* Temperature and Relative Humidity
  *vi.* Air Pressure
  *vii.* Rainfall
  *viii.* Sunshine

It is preferable to use the same standards and codes (mostly international) of the Air Ministry for descriptive recordings. These are given in the *Observer's Handbook*.

i. *General Weather*

  (*a*) Appearance of sky.
  (*b*) Precipitation (rain, drizzle, snow, sleet, hail, etc.).
  (*c*) Electrical phenomena (thunder and lightning).
  (*d*) Atmospheric obscurity (fog, mist, haze, etc.).
  (*e*) State of ground (surface dry, wet, moist, frozen, etc.).
  (*f*) Optical phenomena (rainbow, mirage, lunar halo, etc.).

ii. *Cloud*

  (*a*) Type (see *Observer's Handbook*, plates I–XX or "Cloud photographs from the Clarke collection" a series of post-cards published by the Royal Meteorological Society, 49 Cromwell Road, London, S.W.7).
  (*b*) Amount in oktas, i.e. eighths.
  (*c*) Height at base (compare with known heights of hills, etc. When this is not possible only an estimate can be made, see *Observer's Handbook*).
  (*d*) Speed at which moving: requires a *nephoscope*: see *Observer's Handbook*.
  (*e*) Direction of movement.

iii. *Visibility*

A number of objects each at a standard distance are chosen. A description of the visibility is given according to these distances:

| Not more than | 40 metres | ( 44 yards) | —dense fog. |
|---|---|---|---|
| ,, ,, ,, | 100 ,, | ( 110 ,, ) | —thick fog. |
| ,, ,, ,, | 200 ,, | ( 220 ,, ) | —fog. |
| ,, ,, ,, | 400 ,, | ( 440 ,, ) | —moderate fog. |
| ,, ,, ,, | 1,000 ,, | (1,100 ,, ) | —mist, haze or very poor visibility. |

Not more than  2 kilometres (  1¼ miles)—poor visibility.
,,    ,,    ,,   7      ,,     ( 4⅓  ,,  )—moderate visibility.
,,    ,,    ,,   10     ,,     ( 6¼  ,,  )—good visibility.
,,    ,,    ,,   30     ,,     (18⅔  ,,  )—very good visibility.
,,    ,,    ,,   40     ,,     (25   ,,  )—excellent  visibility.

## iv. *Wind*

(*a*) Direction from which it is coming (vanes can be used).
(*b*) Force (use Beaufort's scale).

| 0 | Calm: | calm; smoke rises vertically. |
|---|---|---|
| 1 | Light air: | direction shown by smoke drift but not by vanes. |
| 2 | Light breeze: | wind felt on face; leaves rustle; ordinary vane moved by wind. |
| 3 | Gentle breeze: | leaves and small twigs in constant motion; wind extends light flag. |
| 4 | Moderate breeze: | raises dust and loose paper; small branches are moved. |
| 5 | Fresh breeze: | small trees in leaf begin to sway; crested wavelets form on inland waters. |
| 6 | Strong breeze: | large branches in motion; whistling heard in telegraph wires; umbrellas used with difficulty. |
| 7 | Moderate gale: | whole trees in motion; inconvenience felt when walking against wind. |
| 8 | Fresh gale: | breaks twigs off trees; generally impedes progress. |
| 9 | Strong gale: | slight structural damage occurs (chimney pots and slates removed). |

| 10 | Whole gale: | seldom experienced inland; trees uprooted; considerable structural damage occurs. |
| 11 | Storm: | very rarely experienced; accompanied by widespread damage. |

## v. *Temperature*

(*a*) Dry. } For determination of relative humidity see
(*b*) Wet bulb. } also p. 74.
(*c*) Maximum.
(*d*) Minimum.
(*e*) Grass minimum.
(*f*) Ground—0–12 in. or any depth as required.

## vi. *Air-pressure*

A continuous recording *barograph* is best, but an ordinary barometer is useful. For accurate readings an instrument calibrated in millibars with an attendant thermometer is usually used; corrections for temperature have to be made for each barometer.

## vii. *Rainfall*

Use only the standard gauge calibrated in millimetres. (25 mm = 1 inch of rainfall or 1 foot of freshly fallen snow).

## viii. *Sunshine*

A recorder is used in which a trace is scorched on a card by the sun's rays which are focussed through a spherical lens (see the *Observer's Handbook*).

## Section I

# LITERATURE AND INFORMATION

Correct identification of plants and animals is as essential in field work as in other branches of Biology. No comprehensive literature exists for naming all the British plants and animals. In some critical groups it is necessary to consult the appropriate specialists.

The problem is to find out what literature is available, and which works are up-to-date, reliable, and worth consulting. The Systematics Association publishes a *Bibliography of Key Works for the Identification of the British Fauna and Flora*. This is obtainable from the Treasurer, c/o The British Museum (Natural History) at the address given in the footnote below.* The last list appeared in 1953, and inevitably does not include certain important works published since then. It is by no means easy to keep up to date with taxonomic literature, but help is usually obtainable from these organisations:

I. *Learned societies*, e.g. Zoological Society of London, Royal Entomological Society of London, Botanical Society of the British Isles, Institute of Biology.

II. *Museums*. See *Directory of Museums and Art Galleries in the British Isles*, by F. S. Markham, published by the Museums Association (1948).

* The officers of the British Museum (Natural History), Cromwell Road, London, S.W.7, undertake indentification of specimens which should be sent carefully packed and with full data of capture (see p. 135). Only specimens should be sent which it has not been possible to identify, and whose names are essential to the work in hand.

III. *Local natural history societies.* See *The Directory of Natural History Societies* (1948) and *First Supplement* (1949), by H. K. Airy Shaw published by the Amateur Entomologists' Society.

IV. *Libraries.*

It is very important to realise that the officers of these organisations, especially of museums, though invariably courteous and helpful in response to requests for information, and for assistance with identifications, are extremely busy people. Approaches should be made to them only when it is absolutely necessary, and after all efforts to solve the problem have been made by the enquirer.

Certain of the larger publishing houses and sellers of new and second-hand books are helpful with queries about literature.

Before embarking on any comprehensive survey or detailed observations on a species it is essential to find out what work, if any, has already been done. The more important works are listed in sections, in—

(*i*) *The Zoological Record* (published by the Zoological Society of London).

(*ii*) *Biological Abstracts* (University of Pennsylvania, Executive and Editorial Offices, 3815 Walnut St., Philadelphia 4, Pa., U.S.A.). This monthly journal gives abstracts of the World's Biological Research Literature under the headings of (*a*) General Biology, (*b*) Basic Medical Sciences, (*c*) Microbiology, Immunology and Parasitology, (*d*) Plant Sciences, (*e*) Animal Sciences.

These are published annually, and amongst others list taxonomic and ecological works.

A list of books and journals, with brief comments, is given in the bibliography on pp. 148–156. These works are intended as a guide, and they have been selected for those with little experience of the literature.

Two points remain to be mentioned.

1. The value of joining a natural history society or a learned society cannot be over-emphasised. It is often through such organisation that personal contacts are made, and these can be of great assistance, because the benefit of experience can be passed on directly to those who are most receptive to making the best use of it.

2. Apart from field work organised by societies, various field courses are run by some educational authorities. Details are available from the Local or County Educational Offices, and some are advertised in the educational journals. The National Institute of Adult Education, 35 Queen Anne Street, London, W.1 will give information about courses at county educational colleges.

Weekly courses in field studies are run by the Field Studies Council at their five centres in Pembrokshire, Shropshire, Suffolk, Surrey and Yorkshire. Details of this organisation, and of courses for Sixth-form pupils, training college students, teachers, amateur naturalists and others are obtainable from the Secretary, at the address given in the footnote on page ix. Courses are also given by the Scottish Field Studies Association, The Secretary, c/o The University, Glasgow, and by Dr. E. A. R. Ennion at the Bird Observatory and Field Station, Monk's House, Seahouses, Northumberland.

## Section J

# BIBLIOGRAPHY

In addition to the books referred to in the text the following lists contain selected works and a section of "key" references to series of publications. New works are published from time to time; notice and reviews of the more useful ones usually appear in various journals including *Nature* (Macmillan), *The Times Educational Supplement, The Times Literary Supplement, Discovery, Country-Side* and *The Countryman*. In addition a list of journals likely to be useful to the field biologist is given. Comments are appended, to which the following abbreviations refer:

I = A good introductory book.
S = Standard work.
A = Advanced Reference work and text-book.
G = General accounts intended for serious, but not heavy, reading (as opposed to a reference work).

## I. Series of Publications*

The subjects covered in these series are sometimes wide and outside the range of the field biologist, but certain volumes are strongly to be recommended. It should be remembered that additional volumes may appear from time to time and publishers if requested will usually keep enquirers informed of forthcoming books, and will supply a list of those already published.

\* Useful leaflets and other publications are issued by various organisations such as the Association of School Natural History Societies, School Nature Study Union, Universities Federation of Animal Welfare. Enquiries should be made.

1. Department of Scientific and Industrial Research Leaflets. Deal with some pests; apply for a list through H.M. Stationery offices or booksellers.

2. Forestry Commission Publications. Animals and plants of economic importance in woodlands. A list of publications can be obtained from The Secretary, 25 Savile Row, London, W.1.

3. Handbooks for the Identification of British Insects. Published by and obtainable from The Secretary, Royal Entomological Society of London, 41 Queen's Gate, London, S.W.7.

4. Ministry of Agriculture and Fisheries Advisory Leaflets. Deal with animal and plant pests; crops, etc., some beneficial species mentioned. A list is obtainable through any of H.M. Stationery offices or booksellers.

5. "New Naturalist" series published by Messrs. Collins, London. Some excellent general reading, covering both plant and animal life. Regional volumes of natural history are published and smaller "monographs" dealing with one or two species, or a specialised aspect of biology.

6. "Observer's Book" series published by Messrs. Frederick Warne & Co. Ltd., London. An excellent introductory series, well illustrated, and helpful for identification of some groups.

7. "Ray Society" publications; obtainable from Messrs. Bernard Quaritch Ltd., London, or direct if a member of the Society. Mainly specialist works in taxonomy of plants and animals. Some useful back numbers are still obtainable.

8. Scientific Publications of the Fresh-water Biological Association obtainable from The Director, The Ferry House, Ambleside, Westmorland.

9. Synopses of the British Fauna. Published by and obtainable from The Secretary, The Linnean Society of London, Burlington House, Piccadilly, London, W.1.

10. "Wayside and Woodland Series" published by Messrs. Frederick Warne & Co. Ltd., London. A useful series for identification of some groups. Well illustrated.

## II. GEOLOGY

1. EVANS, I. O. *The Observer's Book of British Geology*, Frederick Warne & Co. Ltd., London, 1949 (I).
2. HOLMES, A. *Principles of Physical Geology*, Thomas Nelson & Sons Ltd., London, 1944 (S).
3. KIRKALDY, J. F. *General Principles of Geology*, Hutchinson & Co. (Publishers) Ltd., London, 1954 (S).
4. LAKE, P., and RASTALL, R. H. *Text-book of Geology*, Edward Arnold & Co., London, 1941 (S).
5. RAISTRICK, A. *Teach Yourself Geology*, English University Press Ltd., London, 1943 (I).
6. STAMP, L. D. *Britain's Structure and Scenery*, Collins, London, 1946 (G).
7. TAYLOR, H. E. *Wonders of the Earth's Crust*, Sir Isaac Pitman & Son Ltd., London, 1947 (I).
8. WATTS, W. W. *Geology for Beginners*, Macmillan & Co. Ltd., London, 1929 (I).

Journals:

*Proceedings of The Geological Association.*
*The Geological Magazine.*

## III. PEDOLOGY

1. BRADE-BIRKS, S. G. *Good Soil*, English Universities Press Ltd., London, 1949 (I).
2. CLARKE, G. R. *The Study of the Soil in the Field*, Oxford University Press, 1957 (S).
3. COMBER, N. M. *An Introduction to the Scientific Study of the Soil*, Edward Arnold & Co., London, 1936 (S).
4. JACKS, G. V. *Soil*, Thomas Nelson & Sons Ltd., London, 1954 (G).
5. KUBIËNA, W. L. *The Soils of Europe*, Thomas Murby & Co., London, 1953 (A).
6. MOORE, W. G. *The Soil We Live On*, Methuen & Co. Ltd., London, 1950 (I).
7. MORGAN, M. F. *Universal Soil Testing System*, Connecticut Agriculture Experimental Station. (S)—for analysis of the main chemical constituents of soil.

8. ROBINSON, G. W. *Mother Earth*, Thomas Murby & Co., London, 1947 (I).
9. ROBINSON, G. W. *Soils, their Origin, Constitution and Classification*, Thomas Murby & Co., London, 1949 (A).
10. RUSSELL, E. J. *Lessons on Soil*, Cambridge University Press, 1950 (I).
11. RUSSELL E. J. *Soil Conditions and Plant Growth*, Longmans, Green & Co., London, 1950 (A).
12. U.S. Department of Agriculture. *Soil Survey Manual*, 1951 (A).
13. VANSTONE, E. *The Soil and the Plant*, Macmillan & Co. Ltd., London, 1947 (I).

Journals:

*Journal of Soil Science*. (Commonwealth Bureau of Soil Science, Rothamsted Experimental Station, Harpenden, Herts.) O.U.P. Botanical journals should also be consulted.

## IV. GENERAL ECOLOGY

1. BRIMBLE, L. J. F. *Nature Studies for Schools*, Macmillan & Co. Ltd., London, 1951 (I).
2. EDLIN, M. L. *The Changing Wild Life of Britain*, B. T. Batsford Ltd., London, 1952 (G).
3. Neal, E. *Woodland Ecology*, William Heinemann Ltd., London, 1953 (I).
4. NEWBIGIN, M. I. *Plant and Animal Geography*, Methuen & Co. Ltd., London, 1950 (S).
5. STORK, J. W., and RENOUF, L. P. W. *Plant and Animal Ecology*, John Murray, London, 1948 (I).

## V. PLANT ECOLOGY

1. BRACHER, R. *Field Studies in Ecology*, J. W. Arrowsmith, Ltd., Bristol, 1939 (I).
2. DAUBENMIRE, R. F. *Plants and Environment*, John Wiley & Sons, Inc., New York (Chapman & Hall Ltd., London), 1947 (S).
3. GODWIN, H. *The History of the British Flora*, Cambridge University Press, 1956 (S).
4. LEACH, W. *Plant Ecology*, Methuen & Co. Ltd., London, 1949 (S).
5. LOUSLEY, J. E. (editor). *The Changing Flora of Britain*, Botanical Society of the British Isles, 1953 (G).

6. McLean, R. C., and Cook, W. R. I. *Practical Field Ecology*, George Allen & Unwin Ltd., London, 1950 (S).
7. Matthews, J. R. *Origin and Distribution of the British Flora*, Hutchinson & Co. (Publishers) Ltd., London, 1955 (G).
8. Tansley, A. G. *Practical Plant Ecology*, George Allen & Unwin Ltd., London, 1926 (I).
9. Tansley, A. G. *Introduction to Plant Ecology*, George Allen & Unwin Ltd., London, 1946 (I).
10. Tansley, A. G. *Britain's Green Mantle*, George Allen & Unwin Ltd., London, 1949 (G).
11. Tansley, A. G. *The British Islands and their Vegetation*, Cambridge University Press, 1953 (A).

(See also the "New Naturalist" series, Collins)

Journals:

*Annals of Botany*; general papers and book reviews.
*Journal of Ecology*; papers; book reviews.
*New Phytologist*; papers; book reviews.
*Proceedings of the Botanical Society of the British Isles*; general papers; book reviews; abstracts of other journals.
*Transactions of the British Bryological Society*; papers on mosses and liverworts; book reviews and abstracts of other journals.
*Transactions of the British Mycological Society*; papers on fungi and lichens; book reviews.
*Watsonia*; papers (mostly taxonomic).

## VI. Animal Ecology

1. Allee, W. V., Emerson, A. E., Park, O., Park, T., and Schmidt, K. P. *Principles of Animal Ecology*, Saunders & Co., Philadelphia, 1949 (A).
2. Allee, W. C., Schmidt, K. P. and Hesse, R. *Ecological Animal Geography*, John Wiley & Sons, Inc., New York (Chapman & Hall Ltd., London), 1951 (A).
3. Beirne. *The Origin and History of the British Fauna*, Methuen & Co. Ltd., London, 1952 (G).
4. Besly, M. A., and Meyer, G. R. *Field Work in Animal Biology*, Methuen & Co. Ltd., London, 1955 (I).
5. Chapman, R. N. *Animal Ecology*, McGraw-Hill Book Co. Inc., New York, 1931 (A).

6. DOWDESWELL, W. H. *Animal Ecology*, Methuen & Co. Ltd., London, 1952 (I) (a good book with a useful bibliography).
7. ELTON, C. *Animal Ecology*, Sidgwick & Jackson, Ltd., London, 1927 (G).
8. ELTON, C. *The Ecology of Animals*, Methuen & Co. Ltd., London, 1950 (G).
9. MACFADYEN, A. *Animal Ecology: Aims and Methods*, Sir Isaac Pitman & Sons Ltd., London, 1957 (A).
10. PEARSE, A. S. *Animal Ecology*, McGraw-Hill Book Co. Inc., New York, 1939 (A).

(See also the "New Naturalist" series, Collins)

Journals:

*Bulletin of the Amateur Entomologists' Society*; papers, book reviews.

*Entomologists' Gazette*; papers, book reviews.

*Journal of Animal Ecology*; papers, book reviews, Abstracts of papers covering fifty-two journals. (For other journals not mentioned here see the Journal of Animal Ecology.)

## VII. GENERAL WORKS; EACH COVERS A NUMBER OF TAXONOMIC GROUPS AND THEIR BIOLOGY

1. BRITISH MUSEUM (NATURAL HISTORY). *Instructions for Collectors 9A* (Invertebrates other than insects) and (1954) No. *4A* (Insects), 1940—useful summaries of chief characters of groups (I).
2. DALE, A. *Patterns of Life*, William Heinemann Ltd., London, 1949 (I).
3. FRIEDLANDER, C. P., and PRIEST, D. A. *Insects and Spiders*, Sir Isaac Pitman & Sons Ltd., London, 1955 (I).
4. KEVAN, D. K. McE. (editor). *Soil Zoology*, Butterworths Publications Ltd., London, 1955 (I).
5. LULHAM, R. *Introduction to Zoology through Nature Study*, MacMillan & Co. Ltd., London, 1949 (I).
6. SANDARS, E. *An Insect Book for the Pocket*, Oxford University Press, 1946 (I).
7. SAVOY, T. H. *The World of Small Animals*, University of London Press, 1955 (I).

(See also the "New Naturalist" series, Collins)

## VIII. General Works on Fresh-Water Biology

1. CARPENTER, K. *Life in Inland Waters*, Sidgwood & Jackson Ltd., London, 1928 (S).
2. GARNETT, W. J. *Fresh-water Microscopy*, Constable & Co. Ltd., London, 1953 (S).
3. MELLANBY, H. *Animal Life in Fresh-water*, Methuen & Co. Ltd., London, 1951 (I).
4. NEEDHAM, J. G., and NEEDHAM, P. R. *A Guide to the Study of Fresh-water Biology*, Comstock Publishing Co. Inc., New York, 1941 (S).
5. POPHAM, E. J. *Some Aspects of Life in Fresh-water*, Heinemann Ltd., London, 1955 (I).
6. WARD, H. B., and WHIPPLE, G. C. *Fresh-water Biology*, John Wiley & Sons, Inc., New York (Chapman & Hall Ltd., London), 1918 (S).

(See also the "New Naturalist" series, Collins)

## IX. Insects

1. BEIRNE, B. P. *Collecting, Preparing and Preserving Insects*, Canada Department of Agriculture, 1955 (S).
2. DAGLISH, E. F. *Name this Insect*, J. M. Dent & Sons Ltd., London, 1952 (I).
3. GREENE, J. *The Insect Hunter's Companion*, Adlard & Son & West Newman Ltd., London, 1924 (S). Useful for general field methods and for certain museum techniques.
4. IMMS, A. D. *Outlines of Entomology*, Methuen & Co. Ltd., London, 1949 (S).
5. IMMS, A. D. *Textbook of Entomology*, Methuen & Co. Ltd., London, 1957.
6. JARDINE, N. K. *The Dictionary of Entomology*, Janson & Sons, London, n.d. (S).
7. KLOET, G. S., and HINCKS, W. D. *A Check List of British Insects*, published by the authors, Stockport, 1945. Gives good list of references (S).
8. MORETON, B. D. *Guide to British Insects*, Macmillan & Co. Ltd., London, 1950 (S).
9. SANDARS, E. *An Insect Book for the Pocket*, Oxford University Press, 1946 (I).

(See also the "New Naturalist" series, Collins, and publications by the Amateur Entomologists' Society).

A full list of journals is given in *Journal of Animal Ecology*.

## X. The Sea-shore and Estuaries

1. BARRETT, J. H., and YONGE, C. M. *Guide to the Seashore*, Collins, London, 1958 (I).
2. BESLY, M. A., and MEYER, G. R. *Field Work in Animal Biology*, Methuen & Co. Ltd., London, 1955 (I).
3. EALES, N. B. *The Littoral Fauna of Great Britain*, Cambridge University Press, 1939 (S).
4. FLATTELY, F. W., and WALTON, C. L. *The Biology of the Seashore*, Sidgwick & Jackson, London, 1922 (S).
5. NEWTON, L. *A Handbook of the British Seaweeds*, British Museum (Natural History), 1931 (S).
6. RUSSEL, F. S., and YONGE, C. M. *The Seas*, Warne, London, 1947 (G).
7. WILSON, D. P. *Life of the Shore and Shallow Sea*, Ivor Nicholson & Watson, London, 1935 (S).
8. WILSON, D. P. *They Live in the Sea*, Collins, London, 1947 (G).
9. YONGE, C. M. *British Marine Life* (Britain in Pictures), Collins; London, 1946. (Reprinted in Nature in Britain, ed., W. J. Turner) (G).
10. YONGE, C. M. *The Sea Shore*, Collins, London, 1949 (G).
    (See also below, XI, 2, 9A. Instructions for collectors.)

Journals:
*Journal of the Marine Biological Association of the United Kingdom.* Abstracts of memoirs; few book reviews. See also below, XI, 8 —additional list of journals.

## XI. Useful Publications

1. THE BIOLOGICAL COUNCIL—A list of abbreviations of the titles of biological journals. (Selected, by permission from the *World List of Scientific Periodicals*); obtainable from H. K. Lewis & Co. Ltd., 136 Gower Street, London, W.C.1.
2. BRITISH MUSEUM (NATURAL HISTORY). *Instructions for Collectors 9A* (Invertebrates other than Insects) 1940, and No. *4A* (Insects) 1954. Methods of preservation.
3. FAGG, C. C. and HUTCHINGS, G. E. *An Introduction to Regional Surveying*, Cambridge University Press, 1930.
4. GREEN, T. L. *The Teaching and Learning of Biology*, Allman & Son (Publishers) Ltd., London, 1954. Useful for some aspects of biology including field work.

5. KNIGHT, M. *The Young Field Naturalists' Guide*, G. Bell & Sons, Ltd., London, 1952.
6. National Book League (7 Albermarle Street, London, W.1) and National Federation of Young Farmers' Clubs (55 Gower Street, London, W.C.1). Country Books—A list of bibliographies and the organisations which publish them. (Produced jointly by the N.B.L. and N.F.Y.F.C.).
7. *School Science Review.* Contains biological articles, and book reviews.
8. In addition to the journals listed in the preceding sections there are others which from time to time contain papers of importance to the field worker; amongst the more important ones are: *Annals and Magazine of Natural History*; *Proceedings of the Malacological Society*; *Transactions and Proceedings of the Zoological Society of London*; *Journal and Proceedings of the Linnean Society of London*; *Quarterly Journal of Microscopical Science*; *Journal of the Quekett Microscopical Club.*
9. HENDERSON, I. F. & W. D. *Dictionary of Scientific Terms*, 6th edition by J. H. Keaneth, London, Oliver & Boyd, 1957.
10. JAEGER, E. C. *A Source Book of Biological Names and Terms*, Illinois, Charles C. Thomas, 1950.
11. SAYERS, N. A. *A Biological Glossary*, University of London Press Ltd., 1951.

## XII. PHOTOGRAPHY

The best way to learn photography is to have the tuition of an experienced person; useful books are:

1. COTT, H. B. *Zoological Photography in Practice*, The Fountain Press, London, 1956 (S).
2. PIKE, O. G. *Nature and Camera*, Focal Press Ltd., London, 1944 (S).

Articles appear from time to time in the *Amateur Photographer*.

## XIII. MAPS

1. BIRCH, T. W. *Maps Topographical and Statistical*, Oxford University Press, 1952 (S).
2. CAVE, R. P. *Elementary Map Reading*, Methuen & Co. Ltd., London, 1953 (I).

3. H.M. ORDNANCE SURVEY. Particulars of all ordnance maps, geological and others published, are obtainable through H.M. Stationery offices or book-sellers. (Maps used by certain educational institutes can be obtained at reduced prices. Ask for particulars).

4. HIGGINS, A. L. *Elementary Surveying*, Longmans, Green & Co., London, 1946 (I).

5. LABORDE, E. D. *Popular Map Reading*, Cambridge University Press, 1928 (I).

6. MONKHOUSE, J. F., and WILKINSON, H. R. *Maps and Diagrams*, Methuen & Co. Ltd., London, 1952 (S).

7. RICHARDSON, W. A. *Surveying for Schools and Scouts*, George Philip & Son, Ltd., London, 1924 (I).

8. THOENE, C. *The Map and the Compass*, Edward Stanford Ltd., London, 1955 (I).

## XIV. WEATHER

1. BARTLETT, D., and BARTLETT, K. *Signpost to the Weather*, Edward Stanford, Ltd., London, 1949 (I).

2. BILHAM, E. G. *The Climate of the British Isles*, Macmillan & Co. Ltd., London, 1938 (S).

4. MANLEY, G. *Climate and the British Scene*, Collins, London, 1952 (G).

3. H.M.S.O. *The Book of Normals*. Average climatic figures given for the British Isles.

Journals:

*Weather* (the Royal Meteorological Society), papers, book reviews.

## XV. ELEMENTARY STATISTICS

1. BROOKES, B. C., and DICK, W. F. L. *Introduction to Statistical Method*, William Heinemann Ltd., London, 1955 (I).

2. BROWNLEA, K. A. *Industrial Experimentation*, H.M.S.O., 1949 (S).

3. CHAMBERS, E. G. *Statistical Calculations for Beginners*, Cambridge University Press, 1940 (I).

4. MATHER, K. *Statistical Analysis in Biology*, Methuen & Co. Ltd., London, 1949 (S).

# INDEX

Figures in *italics* refer to pages on which illustrations occur. Those in **heavy type** indicate major references.